ROME
THE SWEET
TEMPESTUOUS LIFE

ROME

THE SWEET TEMPESTUOUS LIFE

Paul Hofmann

CONGDON & LATTÈS   New York

Library of Congress Cataloging in Publication Data

Hofmann, Paul, 1912–
Rome—the sweet, tempestuous life.
1. Rome (Italy)—Social life and customs—Addresses,
essays, lectures. I. Title.
DG807.6.H63 1981 945'.632092 81-15110 AACR2

ISBN 0-86553-033-5
ISBN 0-312-92737-1 (St. Martin's Press)

Published by Congdon & Lattès, Inc.
Empire State Building, New York, N.Y. 10001

Distributed by St. Martin's Press
175 Fifth Avenue, New York, N.Y. 10010

Published simultaneously in Canada by Thomas Nelson & Sons Limited
81 Curlew Drive, Don Mills, Ontario M3A 2R1

CONTENTS

ROME
THE SWEET
TEMPESTUOUS LIFE

ROMAN NEW YEAR

At one A.M. on the New Year's Eve that began the eighties, the biggest bang—*botto*—came like a bursting mortar shell. The powerful blast shook the neighborhood and made the glasses on our table jump. It was loud enough to awaken hundreds of Romans who, after watching a soporific New Year's Eve show on state television and drinking champagne, had already gone to bed. Some who were still celebrating came out briefly on their balconies, cheered the unknown bomber, and quickly withdrew from the cold.

But the celebration that night was a tame affair compared with the threatening din of past New Year's Eves. I had spent one of them, during the sixties, in the same apartment from which I welcomed 1980, an apartment on the slope of Monte Mario from which there is a sweeping view of the city: in the foreground, the dark silhouette of St. Peter's and the Vatican palaces with all windows dark; the cupolas, towers, and roofscape of the historic center spreading out to the southern suburbs; the lights of the towns in the Alban Hills on the horizon. That night, I had stood on the terrace and watched the city errupt like a volcano from long before midnight till long after. Hundreds of heavy charges had gone off. Shots were fired into the air, and even the stutter of automatic weapons was heard. Bottles and discarded crockery, pots, pans, burned-out light bulbs, even a rusty bathtub—household goods presumably saved all year for this occasion—sailed out of innumerable windows and crashed on the pavement below. For at least a couple of hours Rome had sounded like a combat zone in the Vietnam war, which was then on.

The morning after that party, I learned that a youngster had died of wounds from a homemade petard he had set off. A hundred other Romans had suffered injuries in similar incidents. When a friend of mine left a party in the Flaminio district to look for his parked car, he found the windshield shattered and the roof caved in under the impact of a cluster of empty wine bottles. I myself saw the shattered remains of a toilet bowl on the sidewalk of the Via Trionfale, obviously flung from a considerable height and clearly capable of killing somebody.

But in those days few Romans would have risked venturing out into the streets on foot during the New Year's Eve festivities. This isn't a city where a crowd gathers in some central square to wait for the clock to strike twelve, fraternizing with unknown people and drinking bubbly out of paper cups. And few autos would move through the city until the sanitation department, its personnel alerted for the emergency, was able to clear at least the major thoroughfares of the debris.

This year, however, there was little danger of a flat tire— no heaps of broken bottles and plates lined the streets. And this year there were very few big blasts. Why the pyrotechnic restraint? I wondered. It could hardly have been respect for the law. For decades, at the end of every year, the authorities have warned the population not to indulge in the custom of the big bangs, which they invariably brand as "uncivil." Stiff fines, even jail are said to await anyone caught manufacturing, selling, or possessing the big firecrackers needed for the *botti*. But the penalties are rarely enforced, and Romans have regularly ignored the ban on blasting out the old year.

Early in January 1980, the police said they had arrested nine people for trafficking in explosives for the illegal *botti*. But still, it was well known that anybody who wanted to buy large firecrackers could easily get them from a friend of the

2

news vendor at the street corner or a relative of the woman who sells vegetables.

The theory that Romans just didn't feel like celebrating the New Year doesn't stand up; restaurants, nightclubs, discotheques all did roaring business. I myself had to choose among five invitations to private parties in various sections of the city.

One explanation may be that Rome had become traumatized by the many bombings, shootings, and other terrorist violence it had lately witnessed. Italians in general can put up with more noise than people in northern countries do, even seem to enjoy the onslaught to their ears; but here in the capital, at least, it may be that an increasing number of residents no longer want to hear sounds reminding them of weaponry.

Whatever the reason, the subdued mood was apparently confined to Rome. Friends who spent New Year's Eve in Naples, only three hours by car to the south, reported that the roar at midnight suggested a bombardment from the air and the sea combined with an outbreak of nearby Mt. Vesuvius. The police stated that 158 persons were injured by explosives and that one man was shot in the head by a neighbor who meant to fire his rifle into the air. *This* was New Year's Eve in the Roman style of yesteryear! (But eleven months later, Naples was hit by an earthquake that killed three thousand people in a vast area in southern Italy. New Year's Eve in 1981 was as subdued as Rome's in 1980.)

So our gathering in the Monte Mario apartment was generally peaceful. At midnight, of course, red and green rockets shot into the air from points all over the city. Flares lit up rooftops and terraces, firecrackers crepitated, and shivering revelers on balconies or in open windows laughed and yelled. But the celebration was a far cry from those of years past. The final *botto* at one A.M. seemed more an afterthought than a grand finale, a postscript to a tradition in rapid decline.

3

CHURCH AND STATE

The lackluster New Year's Eve festivities were followed by the inevitable morning-after messages.

"You will see we shall manage to get out of the tunnel of violence, unemployment, and economic recession," said the president of the republic on television.

At noon, the Pope showed himself in an open window on the third floor of the Apostolic Palace, pointed to the clear sky, and told the crowd in St. Peter's Square, "The sun will stay with us all year!" (It rained in the afternoon.)

And the mayor of Rome, Luigi Petroselli, declared that the city was at a crossroads, "a crossroads between decadence and further decay or recovery." He named the city's worst evils—terrorism, drug addiction, 70,000 unemployed youths, 800,000 Romans in substandard dwellings. He charged that reckless and corrupt real estate developers had enjoyed free rein for decades—when city hall was in the hands of the Christian Democrats—and insisted nevertheless that the present left-wing administration must collaborate with the Catholic Party, now the largest group in the municipal parliament, if it wanted to solve Rome's daunting problems.

Mayor Petroselli, former secretary of the local Communist Party, is the second mayor in Rome's first Communist-dominated administration. Early in January he called on the Pope in the Vatican to offer his and the city government's official good wishes to the head of the church.

Pictures in the newspapers showed Mayor Petroselli, in a

dark suit and a white shirt, his hands linked over his stomach as if in prayer, standing deferentially in front of the white-clad pontiff, who inspects a city medal he has just been given by his visitor.

Outside, in St. Peter's Square, the police meanwhile were dispersing a small group of Radical Party militants there to protest Rome's first citizen "kissing the sacred slipper" of the Pope. The Communist mayor didn't exactly do that (nobody does nowadays), but there was no doubt that the city's civil authorities were paying homage to the bishop of Rome.

Nevertheless, a representative of the Radical Party, a small but vocal movement that fights, among other things, for strict separation between church and state, accompanied the mayor during his Vatican audience, and the Pope good-naturedly joked with the spokesman for anticlericalism. City commissioners and council members of all other forces in the municipal parliament were also present.

The tribute to the Pope by the Communist apparatchik who recently became mayor, Machiavellian though it may be, reflects the unique relationship between secular Rome and the Vatican. In theory, the headquarters of the church is an independent, sovereign state, carved out of the Italian capital in 1929. Actually, the two interpenetrate in permanent, close, and checkered symbiosis.

For instance, the church is landlord to thousands of Roman families who live all over the city in buildings owned by the Vatican or by institutions affiliated with it—religious orders, monasteries, convents, colleges, congregations, and chapters. Distinctions as to where the Vatican ends and the church in Italy and Rome begins are hard to draw. It's like a mighty naval force at sea—aircraft carrier and command vessel at the center, and cruisers, destroyers, minesweepers, submarines, and support craft all around. Some of the units seem autonomous but receive radioed orders from the commanding admiral. The formation changes its aspect depending on the angle from which one looks at it.

So does the papal establishment in Rome. At times it is

5

called the State of Vatican City, at other times the Holy See or the Roman Curia. As in a multinational conglomerate, officials hailing from various parts of the world hold jobs in interlocking corporate bodies. Funds are moved around to avoid the host country's tax bite. Corporate organization charts are confusing, dividing lines vague and often illusory.

The Pope is not only the head of the church throughout the world, he is also bishop of Rome, with direct power over every parish priest, assistant pastor, basilica, and chapel in his own diocese. He is like an admiral who takes time out of his command duties to helicopter to a cruiser in his fleet, where he gives a pep talk to the seamen, inspects their quarters, and samples their rations.

The Vatican has appendages in various parts of the city, outlying churches and palaces that are considered extraterritorial, meaning that Italian authorities have no control over them. Most of the three thousand priests, nuns, and nonecclesiastical personnel who earn stipends, salaries, or wages in the Vatican live outside its walls. After work they go home to their cells in a monastery or to apartments scattered throughout the city. Quite a number of Vatican employees enjoy quarters in church-owned buildings and pay rents much lower than those with which Rome's less fortunate residents have to cope.

If one walks past the Gate of St. Anna, one of the four main entrances to the walled Vatican City, in the afternoon, one may see women with loaded shopping carts coming out. They have just bought groceries at the Vatican commissary, a well-stocked supermarket that doesn't advertise, pays no Italian taxes or import duties, and undersells all stores in the Rome that lies outside the old papal ramparts.

At one time not long ago more than ten thousand Roman families held the coveted cards that entitled them to shop in the pontifical supermarket. The credentials would often be lent for a day to some friend who really had no right to patronize the Vatican commissary but needed a few bottles of cut-rate Scotch whiskey or some cartons of American

6

cigarettes or a Swiss cardigan. The substitute secretary of state under Pope Paul VI, Monsignor Giovanni Benelli, a power-loving disciplinarian from Tuscany who later became cardinal archbishop of Florence, weeded out a great number of the shopping cards. He was unmoved by the howls and teeth-gnashing of those cast out of the Vatican shopping paradise.

Yet a young intellectual with political views far to the left of the Communist Party boasted to me recently that his mother was still making periodic shopping trips to the papal supermarket on the strength of his late father's service as a doctor in a church-run hospital outside the Vatican.

Romans and well-advised foreigners who have letters or packages to send abroad will put up with an hour's bus ride to mail them at the Vatican post office. Nobody trusts the Italian postal service. Mail handed to the Vatican is loaded on a truck every night and taken to Fiumicino Airport, whence it is flown to Switzerland for forwarding.

Unfortunately, the system doesn't work for incoming items to addresses outside the Vatican. An airmail letter from Western Europe or the United States to the Italian capital may take a few days or a month, depending on postal strikes and other vagaries.

The Vatican issues its well-designed mail stamps in sets that follow one another in rapid succession. Sales of the papal stamps to collectors and to those who actually use the Vatican postal service produce sizable revenue, perhaps as much as $20 million a year.

Although it depends mainly on funds contributed from rich dioceses in the United States, West Germany, and elsewhere, the Vatican's lucrative postal service is not its only local source of revenue. The Vatican bank, bashfully christened the Institute for the Works of Religion and hidden away in an old tower, is profitable too. (A painful exception occurred in 1974, when it was hurt in the collapse of the international financial empire of Michele Sindona, a presumed money wizard from Sicily who had counseled the

Vatican in reshuffling its investment portfolio.) The Vatican usually says that its bank primarily takes care of the assets and transactions of religious orders and other church bodies, but Romans of no ecclesiastical standing whatsoever sometimes own up to doing business with the Pope's money-men.

I have checks drawn on my own bank account in New York which were returned, paid, with the stamp of the Institute for the Works of Religion on their backs. But these checks were presented for collection to Italian financial institutions without any known Vatican ties. Where did the Pope's bank come in?

The Vatican connection shows up in many matters here where one wouldn't expect to see it. Not only bankers but also Roman lawyers, scientists, scholars, businessmen, government officials, and politicians have friends in the pontifical enclave whom they can call by phone and ask for favors. And the traffic is two-way. The Pope himself, his aides, and other people in the Vatican are in daily touch, directly or by phone, with innumerable Romans, some influential and some humble. Thus, ordinary residents often know a lot about the pontiff, the papal household, the curial bureaucracy, and the personal affairs of high Vatican personages that even cardinals and archbishops don't know.

When the Communist mayor and the Polish Pope met for the ritual New Year's wishes, they already knew a great deal about each other. They also knew they needed each other. The Vatican is not only a major employer and the city's leading landlord and real estate owner, it is also an important Roman industry. Millions of dollars are spent in the city every year by pilgrims and tourists who come primarily to see the Pope.

On the other hand, the Roman Catholic Church wouldn't be what it is without Rome as its headquarters. No other world religion has a comparable center. The World War II documents that the Vatican has seen fit to publish (many are still kept in secret archives) show that a major concern of

Pope Pius XII, and apparently the principal aim of his diplomatic activities from 1939 to 1944, was to prevent damage to Rome by military action. The wartime Pope unceasingly appealed to the belligerents to recognize Rome as an "open city," and it is mainly owing to his pleas that the Italian capital got away with only a few bombings of its outskirts by the Allied air forces, although Rome served as a supply center and transport hub for the Nazi armies. When the Nazis gave up the city in June 1944, they didn't even blow up the bridges across the Tiber River.

Many Romans have a gut feeling that the presence of the papacy in their midst may again prevent the worst, no matter what happens elsewhere in the world. In the city government's January audience with the Pope, Mayor Petroselli kept his hands reverently folded as the pontiff recalled again that he had "come from far away" and wanted to deepen his knowledge of all facets of city life. The pontiff omitted, as most of his predecessors on this occasion had not, any reference to the "sacred character" of Rome—a phrase contained in the 1929 treaty on church-state relations, the concordat. The concordat stated that in view of the "sacred character of the Eternal City, episcopal see of the supreme pontiff, center of the catholic world and destination of pilgrimages, the Italian government will undertake to prevent anything in Rome that might be in conflict with the said character."

Pope Pius XII invoked this provision to demand that Italian authorities ban earthy films and pornography in the city. The Pope from Poland, who almost every Sunday visits another neighborhood of his own diocese, refrained from mentioning its sacred character, perhaps because he knows very well that the Romans are not saints.

FADING WITCH

On the way to the traditional Epiphany fair in the Piazza Navona, I ran into another, more modern and frequent, local custom—a purse snatching. The *scippo,* which in the Roman vernacular is the technical term for the operation, was pulled off with consummate elegance and without violence.

The target was an elderly German-speaking woman who might have been a guest in a pilgrims' hostel rather than a tourist on a pleasure trip. She seemed not to be immediately aware of what had happened to her, and spent the first few seconds looking for her handbag on the pavement.

Then, with the awful realization that her bag had been eased from under her arm and grabbed by someone in a small car that was already thirty steps away, she started screeching. Too late. From the narrow Via della Stelletta, where the *scippo* had occurred, the small Fiat turned into the Via della Scrofa. I ran after the car, but when I reached the corner the auto had already disappeared in the traffic or had turned into another side street. Nobody had a chance to take down the license plate number, which would have been of little use anyway, since the Fiat was probably stolen and would be abandoned a little later, perhaps after a couple of other quick *scippi.*

Two young foreigners, maybe Dutchmen or Scandinavians, were also witnesses, though they didn't understand right away what they were seeing. Between screams, the victim explained to them in German and body language how she had been robbed, and that her passport and all her money were in the bag.

The two men started shouting, *"Italiani, bandidos!"* and other invective in what they must have thought was Italian. Their yells and the woman's continuing screams caused people all around to open windows and come out of stores to see what the fuss was all about. When they heard the insults to their nation, there was palpable hostility toward the foreign trio.

A heavyset middle-aged man who had stepped out of a doorway said in a rich basso: *"Aoh,* leave the Italians alone, you big drunkards! If you can't hold the wine, go back to where you came from. We don't need you here." Romans as a rule are not chauvinistic but, like most people, resent ethnic disparagement from outsiders.

Only slowly did it dawn on the angry audience that the foreigners weren't drunk, and that a local artist of the *scippo* had just given a performance. The victim didn't even remember whether the hand that reached out of the small Fiat belonged to a man or a woman. Until recently, most bag snatchings were done by youngsters on motor scooters or motorcycles. Lately, many *scippatori,* usually working in tandems, have graduated to autos.

I told the foreign woman and the two men who were taking care of her that they'd find the nearest *carabiniere* on guard duty outside the Palazzo Madama, the Senate building down the Via della Scrofa, but that they would be asked to go to the police station to make a statement. It would be added to hundreds of other recent complaints about *scippi.*

On to the Piazza Navona. The oblong square whose shape recalls the ancient racecourse on which it was built was filled with people milling between rows of stands where candy, toys, souvenirs, pop records, and junk were being sold. Quite a few of the vendors appeared to be North Africans. There were also shooting galleries and booths with new electronic games. Many grown-up men shoved away youngsters so they could match their wits with the circuitry themselves.

On sale everywhere were gauze bags in the form of stockings, containing chocolates, gumdrops, rag dolls, and knickknacks. They were reminders of the time, a couple of generations past, when children in Rome used to hang stockings at the fireplace or over the kitchen range the evening of January 5. A horrible-looking but good-natured witch, the Befana, would come down the chimney at night and put sweets and toys into the stockings of good boys and girls while stuffing those of bad ones with coal.

The name of the Befana is derived, through popular etymology, from Epiphany, the church commemoration of the coming of the Magi and the baptism of Jesus. How the three Wise Men from the East, bearing gifts, were transmogrified into a hag is a folkloric mystery. The Befana is a specifically Roman figure; children in Milan, for instance, were always told their toys were brought by the infant Jesus.

Roman idiom has kept the word *befana* as an unflattering way of referring to an unattractive, not necessarily old, woman. The custom of giving children toys for Epiphany long ago faded. The witch is riding on her broomstick into oblivion, while the consumer society focuses on Christmas.

A few years ago, January 6 was among the dates struck from the list of national holidays because Parliament decided that Italy had too many days of rest. The church now observes the feast of Epiphany on the Sunday nearest to January 6, and the Piazza Navona is almost the only spot in the city that keeps the tradition of the witch alive.

But what was once a children's fable has become a happening mainly for teenagers and young adults. As early dusk settled on the piazza, families with toddlers went home and packs of youths took over. There was horseplay with a lot of laughter, shouting, and jostling. Police plainclothesmen, far from unobtrusive, combed the crowd.

Earlier in the day, the plainclothesmen had taken their stations in the Piazza Navona and had already started looking for notorious pickpockets, drug pushers, and other people listed in the police files. The baroque square has long been a marketplace for Rome's growing narcotics traffic, and a hangout for junkies.

Yet the Piazza Navona has remained the one wide-open space in a warren of cramped downtown streets where mothers can take their children to play, and where elderly residents of the densely populated neighborhood can sit on stone benches in the sun in winter and in the shade in summer. Since city hall closed the square to motor traffic it has become a recreation center.

A Piazza Navona address is highly desirable, provided you live in one of the penthouses that developers, undeterred by zoning regulations, have put on top of the old buildings that enclose the square. While most of the other public squares in the city core have become traffic circuses or parking lots, in the Piazza Navona people of various social classes and population groups, and tourists as well, still lounge and mingle the way noblemen, priests, soldiers, cripples, beggars, and ambiguous characters do in Piranesi prints. The square isn't often as crowded as during the Befana fair, but it remains inhabited by a cross section of Romans during the rest of the year.

Epiphany, the local saying goes, carries all holidays away with it—meaning that after January 6 Christmastime is, alas, definitively over, and a long stretch of weeks without holidays has to be soberly faced.

"The trouble is, the holidays have taken all the money with them," said the burly man whom they call *ingegnere,* engineer, at the espresso bar where I usually drop in for the day's second cup of coffee. The counterman and other patrons nodded in sympathy.

Everybody spends too much money during the festive season, and then must grimly figure out how to pay all the bills that fall due at the beginning of each year: taxes on driver's licenses and autos; car insurance; the fee for the state radio and television system; telephone and utilities; rent; and

13

other undelayable expenses, especially the first promissory notes for Christmas gifts bought on the installment plan.

Employees take an entire morning off to make payments in dauntingly overcrowded banks, post offices, and branches of the Automobile Club. They are lucky if they reach the cashier's windows in a couple of hours. As the eighties began, one in every ten Roman post offices was closed because it had recently been robbed, and the staff refused to work until new steel grilles and electronic surveillance systems could be installed. An Automobile Club office was held up by a couple who had been patiently standing in line until they reached the cashier and could whip out their guns.

Whether one wants to rob the place or just pay one's bills, lining up in Rome requires stamina, alertness, and ingenuity. Radically different from queue-loving Britons and stolid Moscow shoppers, Romans consider a line a challenge to their cunning. First of all, it's never a line here, but a cluster seething with impatience and intrigue. People jockey for inches, try to outsmart their neighbors, or even recklessly push to the front, pretending to have been there before and to have come back only to ask the employee behind the window a quick question. Quarrels erupt. In the ensuing commotion everyone tries a little more footwork.

It's the same way at bus stops, in supermarkets, at the ticket offices of theaters and movie houses, and at the under-staffed check-in counters at Fiumicino Airport. It's also the manner in which Romans drive, always attempting to over-take everyone else, never giving others a break, especially if they are pedestrians.

Speaking of motorists, I wondered that day what had happened to the Befana of the Traffic Policeman. Until a few years ago, on January 6 drivers would stop at the intersections they passed most often, or where they got the most traffic tickets during the year, and put *panettone* cake, a bottle of wine, or a carton of cigarettes, nicely wrapped, on the pavement as a conciliatory tribute to the cops. Businesses used the occasion for some inexpensive promotion by having their delivery vans fan out through the city bringing gifts to the policemen. No longer is there any trace of such motorists' largesse. The custom has vanished as abruptly as the *scippo* victim's handbag that day.

KIDNAPPING, INC.

Early in the year, within three days two kidnappings took place. One victim was the daughter of a well-known tailor and owner of deluxe fashion stores; the other was the son of another wealthy businessman, also in the clothing trade. The circumstances were similar—bandits wearing stocking masks ambushed both victims in their parking garages. The abducted young woman's mother, the man's uncle, and garage attendants were helpless witnesses.

While the two families were waiting for the bandits to make contact and put forward their ransom demands, the press said, "a new Kidnapping, Inc." was operating. There was speculation that it was the same gang that abducted the rich manager of a fuel oil firm a few weeks earlier and released him after collecting $1 million from his relatives.

The idea that an efficient criminal organization was at work appealed to newspaper readers in a city where little else is efficient and works. Actually, the three kidnappings might have been carried out by three different bands, for all that the police knew, which was little. The masked men brandishing revolvers while they took away their victims might have been mercenaries hired by some shadowy group that stayed in the background. The ransom might have been intended, at least in part, to bankroll the terrorist underground. Or the Mafia might have been behind it all.

The fact that the kidnapped woman was twenty-seven years old and about to get married was titillating to the local newspapers. They recalled with relish that less than a year ago the young daughter of an entrepreneur who owns several movie houses was kidnapped, and in captivity was raped by the mastermind of the gang. An earlier Kidnapping, Inc.? His accomplices recorded the sounds of the sexual assault and played the track to the woman's parents over the phone as proof that she was still alive, and probably also to add persuasion to their ransom requests.

The family shelled out $1 million (apparently the standard amount for buying back abducted members of the Roman business class). The mastermind, however, fell into a tender trap. He was arrested when he kept a date, which he foolishly thought would be secret, with the freed movie theater heiress. When the two met in, of all places, the Via Veneto, the police pounced on the gangster. The episode would have made a fitting sequel to Fellini's *La Dolce Vita,* which had helped make the once glamorous boulevard internationally famous.

The victims of the two garage kidnappings belonged to an intermarrying clan whose members control businesses that for decades have been Roman household words. Six years earlier, a second cousin of the kidnapped woman was shot and killed when bandits were raiding a restaurant on the city's northern outskirts. The apparent reason for the slaying: she had refused to hand over her fur coat to the robbers.

Such tidbits of the local kidnapping lore, especially if they arouse prurient interest, are eagerly discussed at the office or the espresso bar. Many Romans barely hide their glee. If Kidnapping, Inc. is able to find out where the big money is and to case its targets so thoroughly, the gangsters are clearly much smarter than the tax office. Rich merchant families with their furs, their jewels, and their big cars (for which there always seem to be convenient parking spaces) aren't wildly popular anyway. "Serves them right," is a frequent comment after yet another kidnapping case.

This gloating over shameful crimes—as if kidnappers were modern Robin Hoods taking from the rich to help, or at least to cheer up, the poor—is in part due to the widespread conviction that the missing persons will eventually come out of their ordeal alive. Such optimism concerning the fate of the garage kidnappees was prompted by reports that the masked abductors in both raids spoke in Roman dialect. The conventional view is that Roman gangsters rarely kill. They aren't Sardinian bandits who have a well-earned reputation for cold cruelty, more than once having slain their kidnapped prisoners after collecting big ransom money.

Sardinian outlawry has a rural base among shepherds who live all year long with their animals, much as their remote ancestors did in prehistoric times, and who know every cave and desolate hut in the barren, empty interior of the island. For hundreds of years, cattle rustling was as endemic in Sardinia as malaria, but kidnapping has lately proved to be much more profitable and even less risky. Cattle will low, sheep will bleat, but human prisoners can be made to shut up. In recent years bandits from the island have been operating on the mainland, even in the Rome region. "They treat their victims like animals," according to one police officer.

As for the garage kidnappings here, some police experts had a disquieting theory: the bandits who took away the young woman and the man were Romans all right, but they were acting on behalf of one of the Sicilian Mafia gangs that were known to have moved into the Rome area. Sicilian and Calabrian mafiosi have long fanned out all over Italy and have been implicated in many crimes in the big industrial cities, especially Milan, Turin, and Rome, where the pickings are much more rewarding than in the destitute south.

If the latest kidnap victims were indeed in Mafia hands, their families and the police were up against astute and ruthless professionals. In an unforgotten 1973 case, a Mafia band kidnapped J. Paul Getty, Jr., grandson of the oil billionaire (who was then still alive) in downtown Rome. The younger Mr. Getty was eventually released near a service station hundreds of miles south of the capital, but only after his abductors had cut off his right ear and sent it to *Il Messaggero* of

Rome as proof that they meant business. Postal services were more than usually disrupted at the time, and the special-delivery letter with its grisly enclosure reached the newspaper office in the capital weeks after it had been mailed. To get the oil heir sprung cost a reported $3.4 million.

A kidnapping requires a lot of manpower. The target must be fingered and the locale cased. A secret prison, often far away, must be prepared. Getaway cars have to be stolen. The gunmen who carry out the actual abduction must get their instructions and may be put through trial runs. The prisoner has to be guarded around the clock, and must be fed. Contacts with the kidnappee's family have to be established, and the ransom money must eventually be picked up. At least half a dozen people may be necessary for a professional job.

The family of an abducted person expects little but trouble from the lawmen. If the police proved powerless in the kidnapping and murder of former Prime Minister Aldo Moro in 1978, would they be able to find and free a merchant's son or daughter? Thousands of policemen, including crack investigators, were mobilized when the ultraleftist Red Brigades kidnapped Mr. Moro, then the favorite candidate for election as Italy's next head of state. After holding him for three months in a secret "people's prison" and subjecting him to a humiliating mock trial, the terrorists assassinated him and, in an ultimate jeering gesture, delivered the body to the heavily guarded downtown area where the nation's two strongest political forces, the Christian Democratic Party and the Communist Party, have their headquarters.

When the garage kidnappings occurred, there were only a few policemen assigned to the cases. The three major arms of Italy's cumbersome law enforcement apparatus—Carabinieri, Public Security Guards, and Finance Guard—together account for about 250,000 men, one for every 225 citizens. As many as 20,000 members of the various police bodies are concentrated in Rome, but few of them are available for fighting common crime. Since the Moro case, antiterrorism vigilance has been enormously stepped up. Thousands of policemen take turns day and night protecting government members and politicians, driving their cars, taking their children to school, walking their dogs, carrying the handbag of the Senate speaker's wife, serving as bodyguards for judges, high civil servants, business tycoons, diplomats, and influential journalists, guarding public buildings and foreign embassies, and providing security for the Pope during his many sallies from the Vatican.

After those two kidnapping cases, a long-familiar routine was again played out, like an opera that has had many performances—overture, first act, second act, intermission, third act, finale. The libretto could be reliably predicted, as follows:

Witnesses of the abduction and relatives of the victims will be questioned by two sets of investigators, Carabinieri and Public Security officers. The two police forces are traditional rivals, and although they are supposed to coordinate their efforts, they tend to conduct separate inquiries and at times withhold evidence from each other. The dream of their commanders, which almost never comes true, is to go on television with a handcuffed mafioso and a shaken ex-kidnappee and announce that it was the Carabinieri, or the Public Security Guards, who through clever detection work and daring action have smashed the gang and freed the prisoner.

A young deputy state prosecutor, chronically overworked, will glance through the police case reports and order the phones of the kidnapping victims' closest relatives tapped. He will then freeze the bank accounts and other assets of the affected families. The theory underlying this procedure is that if the criminals won't get any money, they may eventually admit defeat and release their prisoner without collecting any ransom. In practice, the official antiabduction strategy makes kidnappers, their prisoners, and the families into allies and co-conspirators.

The gangsters may call relatives of their prisoners by

phone, but only to slip false clues to the police monitors. If there is jet noise to be heard in the background during the conversation, the chances are it is a tape recording, meant to make the investigators believe the kidnappers are speaking from a hideout near the airport, whereas they actually are operating out of a basement near the railroad line to Naples.

Serious contacts will take place in quite a different way— not at once, but after some time, when the victim and the family are softened up. The prisoner will be asked by his captors to name a friend or acquaintance. A cautious approach will be made, and eventually discreet liaison will be established under the noses of the police.

The victim's family will meanwhile have raised money from secret bank accounts in Switzerland, from associates or friends, or from loan sharks. No communication can be made by phone or mail, to avoid police interference that may mean another month in captivity.

At last an arrangement with the gangsters will have been negotiated, and the ransom money will be delivered. Of course, the relatives will note the serial numbers of the bank bills, to be reported to the police later. But the kidnappers don't mind. They rely on well-functioning Mafia services to launder hot cash at a hefty rate that is already included in the ransom and is one of the reasons for the current inflation in the abduction industry.

Developments in the two garage kidnappings faithfully stuck to the script. The male victim was freed sixty-seven days later, after his family, docilely following the long-established procedure, paid the usual $1 million. The daughter of the deluxe haberdasher spent forty-nine weeks, nearly a year, in two secret prisons, probably in rural buildings, in the deep south before the oft-interrupted negotiations resulted in her release by the Calabrian mafiosi who had "bought" her from her Roman abductors.

Did she suffer any violence at the hands of the bandits, the reporters wanted to know once the young woman was free. Her eyes narrowing, she hissed, "They respected me." This exchange was guaranteed to enliven conversation in the espresso bars throughout Rome, where the customers had by then nearly forgotten her long captivity.

COFFEE AND ICE CREAM

One morning not long ago I ran into an old acquaintance on the street—Alfredo, the elderly tailor who in Rome's *dolce vita* years made me several suits before he emigrated to the United States. He'd done pretty well in the years since I'd seen him. At first he had worked with his brothers, dressmakers in the Bronx who had left for the States long before him and stayed on after he returned to Rome. ("They have become Americans," he said.) Eventually he had built a thriving business of his own in midtown Manhattan, had won an affluent clientele that appreciated his Roman cut, and, although speaking little English, knew enough to accept no checks or credit cards, just cash. Now he was back, with enough cash accumulated to buy an apartment in the Monteverde section here and a house in the town south of Rome where he was born.

Why had he returned, I wondered. "I missed the espresso," he said. "In Rome I can get out of the house and have a good cup of coffee whenever I feel like it."

Life here would in fact be much more humdrum—to many Romans even intolerably bleak—without the periodic break at the coffee bar next door or on the corner across the street or in the nearby piazza. With several thousand such places dotting every part of the city, most Romans enter an espresso bar at least once a day, if not several times. The cup of strong coffee that the majority of customers drink standing up at the counter may fill a real need for a stimulant in a climate that favors indolence, but more often it is a pretext for noncommittal social contact of the kind Italians like.

Espresso bars, indispensable for the Roman way of life, serve as fast-food outlets, locations for public telephones (although many seem to carry an eternal "Out of Order" sign), and permanent forums for public debate on the soccer championship. Espressos provide opportunities for flirting, legalized and clandestine gambling, and even serious business. Although bottles of vermouth, other aperitifs, and hard liquor are lined up in impressive arrays on the shelves behind the countermen, very little drinking goes on in Roman espresso places.

Many residents here are regulars of two or more espresso bars. I myself go a few times every day to one of four such places in the neighborhood where I live and work, near the Trevi Fountain. Quite often I stroll to a bar near the Pantheon, one famed for the quality of its coffee. Maybe its secret is the particular blend of Brazilian beans, or the water delivered to the block by one of Rome's ancient aqueducts. The water in the Pantheon neighborhood is said to be excellent not only for coffee but also for cooking spaghetti or artichokes.

Whenever I find myself in other parts of the city I don't step into just any espresso bar, but look for one I have been in before. There are perhaps twenty around the city that I frequent.

The word *bar,* which long ago won a place in the Italian language, but which today usually means an espresso shop, has spawned a derivative, *barista,* meaning the person behind the counter. It is primarily a young man's job. A good *barista* has the reflexes of a racing driver and the control of an orchestra conductor. He can simultaneously keep an eye on the coffee oozing from the espresso machine into a battery of cups, pour vermouth and bitters and add a lemon twist to create an *americano,* take a shouted order for a *cappuccino* and a sweet roll, whisper to a woman patron that she looks particularly pretty with her new hairdo, and discuss the miserable showing of the Lazio soccer team with a boisterous cluster of fans while quickly wiping the marble counter clean with his free hand.

The virtuoso performance of the countermen in the face of a surging crowd of customers ensures that service in a Roman espresso place is generally much better than in comparable establishments elsewhere in Europe or the Western Hemisphere. Romans always complain about the many things that don't function in their city, but the espresso bar isn't one of them.

The scene has a certain grace, although it may daze the foreigner. Patrons fire their orders at the *barista,* often two or three at the same time, while jockeying for elbowroom at the counter. There is quick, nervous action, loud talk, laughter, and the bracing smell of freshly ground coffee, all things that make a Roman feel alive and good. With the sheen of its chromium, the surgical white of the countermen's starched jackets and aprons, and the neon lighting, Roman espresso bars are usually cleaner than cafés in Paris, London, or Madrid, and far less impersonal than chain coffeeshops in the United States.

When I first came to Rome, the espresso would drip out of a boilerlike brass affair surmounted by an eagle. One of the several taxes that were then levied on espresso was assessed according to the number of cups the machine could fill with all spouts in action at the same time. The Italian word for spout, *becco,* also means cuckold, which was a source of gleeful double entendre. "How many spouts do you have," the tax inspector was supposed to ask routinely. "If there is a *becco* around, he won't admit it" was the punch line.

In the late 1940s the samovarlike upright brass machines were thrown out together with their eagles, and low-slung chromium models came in. Industrial designers made them look like precision lathes and, later, like computers. Today the old machine with the eagle is an antique like the ringing cash register or the Fiat *topolino* car; I haven't seen an eagle espresso machine for many years, except as a prop in a period movie or play.

Some high-class espresso bars provide a few bar stools along the counter, and quite a few establishments have metal-and-plastic chairs and tables that in the warm season spill out onto the sidewalks and piazzas. A place in my neighborhood even keeps a couple of tables outside on sunny days in winter, never mind how cold it is, and, sure enough, some hardy tourists always sit down and order a bottle of wine, something a Roman would never do.

At tables inside cramped espresso bars, pensioners order a *cappuccino* and a croissant and read *Il Messaggero* from the front-page editorial to the massage parlor ads on the back page. A small-time lawyer may sip his fifth cup of espresso since morning and spread out documents and court forms for a diffident client to sign. But stand-up patrons represent the bulk of bar business in what seems a continual coffee break. The trip from office, workshop, or home to the nearest espresso place, made several times a day, is a beloved Roman ceremony, a habit like girl watching.

If you call a civil servant in a ministry to ask about the status of the import license you want, and his secretary tells you, *"Il dottore* is in conference," he has probably gone out for an espresso. He may have taken a woman colleague with him. Offering a female acquaintance a *cappuccino* or a drink at an espresso place may be a first step that in due course leads to an affair. Flirtation is part of the espresso mystique. Bar operators who know what's good for business pick pretty young women as cashiers, but they see to it that things don't get out of hand. The ideal cashier, from the manager's point of view, is young, attractive, amiable, and enigmatic whenever she is asked—at least a dozen times a day—by some hopeful and clumsy patron, "Do you have a fiancé, signorina?" (Most Romans still say fiancé when they mean boyfriend.)

My friend Pietro, who runs a bar in the Flaminio district,

says turnover shot up by nearly a third after he hired an eighteen-year-old blonde for the cashier's job. "Unfortunately," Pietro recalled, "she started fooling around with customers and kept people waiting while she was setting up dates. The phone near the cash register, which is meant for takeout orders, was increasingly tied up with her personal calls. At the end of her shift, men would wait outside the bar. I finally had to fire her."

Another, related, fixture in Roman life is the *gelateria,* the ice cream emporium, often combined with the espresso bar. One such place is Giolitti's, a few yards from Montecitorio Palace, which houses the Chamber of Deputies. Lawgivers often step out for a few minutes to savor a *gelato.* Christian Democrats and Communists stand side by side there, telling the counterman, "Skip the chocolate, please," or "What's that yellow stuff? Ah, melon? Let me have a dab of it!"

The other day at Giolitti's an austere friend of mine said, making little effort to keep his booming voice down, "Look at our revolutionaries! Who can take those buffoons seriously?" With his chin he pointed at a good-looking man in his forties who was voluptuously licking a cap of whipped cream off an ice cream cone, his velvety eyes melting, an unabashed display of sensual pleasure. He was wearing a gabardine suit, an expensive monogrammed shirt, and moccasins with fancy metal buckles—quite a display from a member of Parliament who represents a movement that calls itself "proletarian," one of the doctrinaire fringe groups to the left of the Communist Party. Giolitti's was already something of an institution when I first arrived in Rome and the grandfather of the present manager was in charge. I was told at the time that he was a remote cousin of Giovanni Giolitti, the left-of-center liberal who had been prime minister for many years. (It was probably Giolitti who, when asked once whether it was difficult to govern Italy, said, "It's not difficult at all. Only, it's useless." The bon mot was later attributed to Mussolini.) Actually, the gelato Giolitti hadn't come from the north, as had the statesman, but from the Ciociaria region between Rome and Naples, which is renowned for its cheeses and other dairy products as well as for its buxom wet nurses. Around 1930 he had opened a milk bar, the Latteria Giolitti, near the Montecitorio Palace, and soon earned a reputation for serving the best *cappuccino* in the neighborhood. *Gelato* was then a summer sideline. Today Giolitti's is a flourishing business with a profusion of chromium equipment, neon lighting, plate glass, and reddish-brown marble, an all-year-long ice cream emporium. In the warm season there are tables and chairs outside in the narrow Via dell' Ufficio del Vicario, and passing autos brush the backs of patrons dipping their spoons into rich gelato compositions. Like other famous *gelato* havens in Rome, Giolitti's always entices its aficionados with new flavors—mango, rhubarb, or, for fun, potato or artichoke—in addition to the classic standbys, vanilla, lemon, pistachio, red currant, zabaglione. Giolitti's has spawned branches in various parts of the city and competes with such other ice cream shrines as Tre Scalini in the Piazza Navona and Rosati's in the Piazza del Popolo.

Romans have fancied cold and sweet sherbets ever since classical times, when the snow and ice needed for them were brought from the high Abruzzi mountains in the interior. *Gelato,* which is more consistent in texture than sherbet, came later, probably from Sicily, whose Arab overlords in the early Middle Ages had a notorious sweet tooth. Italian *gelato* makers have swarmed all over Europe for generations, opening ice cream parlors everywhere. "Italian ices" have long been popular in the New World, too. Yet to innumerable tourists, *gelato* eaten on its home ground is a revelation. From Easter week onward, the cone counters of Giolitti's and other famous *gelato* places are beleaguered by foreign customers, the crowd often three deep. "It's delicious, it tastes different from home, I could live for a week just on *gelato,*" a matron from New Jersey said in the Piazza Navona. If you avoid the industrially produced ice cream brands that come in wrappers or cardboard cups, Roman *gelato* indeed tastes different from place to place because it is turned out by a maze of small firms and neighborhood businesses. Each has its own recipe—a dash of maraschino liqueur, caramel powder, or some other secret ingredient. Health officers and the big-time ice cream industry say that the products of the artisan-type *gelato* makers often have an excessive bacteria count. The "Roman tummy" that occasionally afflicts tourists may sometimes be caused by an ice cream cone, but local residents seem immune, and devour without harm uncounted gallons of creamy sweetness, eatable *dolce vita,* all year round. For thousands of the *popolino,* the low-class "little people," Sunday afternoon doesn't mean watching a soccer game in the stadium or a trip to the seaside. It is the day to walk with one's entire family—grandparents, parents, children—to the neighborhood *gelateria* after the siesta. They all sit around a small table on the sidewalk, fussily choose among the available flavors and confections, and then relish what they have selected. This is the way Salvatore has spent virtually all his Sunday afternoons from April to October during the last twenty years. Salvatore is a messenger for one of the big labor unions. During the week he walks around the city, delivering urgent letters to the employers' confederation, government departments, and political parties, or press releases to the news media. I have always been struck by the way Salvatore talks about his union. "We have issued standby orders to the rank and file to be ready for a strike," he says, or "We are preparing for an all-night session with management representatives." He seems to conceive of himself as an avant-garde fighter in the class struggle. Salvatore lives placidly with his wife, their two children, and his mother in a cramped apartment near the Vatican. During the long Roman outdoor season they all stroll to the broad Via Cola di Rienzo every Sunday afternoon for their ritual *gelato* session; in winter they go to a basement pizzeria on the Piazza Risorgimento. Salvatore's mother can't walk very far because she is arthritic, and Salvatore is happy to be seated on his day of rest after trotting around the city all week. Improbable as it sounds, Salvatore, now in his late forties, has never been out of Rome since the army sent him home from military service in Siena. During vacations he sleeps a little longer in the morning than usual, putters about the house, and goes to the gardens around the Castel Sant'Angelo to read the newspaper or just sit and stare. There are many middle-aged and elderly Romans of the *popolino* who live this way and are quite happy—a stroll around the neighborhood, a chat with an acquaintance, a visit to the wine shop or the *gelato* place. Youngsters growing up in this ambiance, however, usually expect more of life than TV and Sunday *gelato*. Salvatore's son and daughter, twelve and thirteen years old, still enjoy their ice cream, but they talk all the time about motor scooters and plans to go camping at the seaside next summer. For the time being they content themselves with movies after the *gelato*. Salvatore's wife says *gelato* is "my only vice." At the end of her daily shopping tour—to the outdoor market for eggs and vegetables, to the butcher's, to the bakery—she stops at the dairy place in front of their apartment house to buy the day's supply of milk and reward herself with a big cone of vanilla and coffee ice cream. She takes a second cone to her mother-in-law, who has stayed at home, "and I'm always tempted to lick a bit off it," she confesses when the old woman is out of earshot. Vice or self-indulgence, the Roman *gelato* sweetens the life of the clergy, too. One of the espresso bars in my neighborhood is justly praised for its *granita di caffè* with whipped cream and other ice cream specialties, and it has a devoted clientele of priests. Among them are students at the Pontifical North American College. They have been sent to Rome by bishops in the United States to take postgraduate courses in theology and pastoral disciplines.

In the espresso bar I can gauge the progress of the current course program. At its beginning, just one or two of the young American priests will sneak out of the college building a block away for a quick *gelato*. Toward the end of the program, the bar is crowded in the early afternoon with American ecclesiastics who order their favorite flavors with the linguistic ease and gustatory sophistication of any home-grown Roman.

TOWN AND FEW GOWNS
AT THE QUADRANGLE

Quite often I go out around noon, and whenever I leave the house at that hour I run into swarms of young men in open-necked shirts and blue jeans, huddling in windbreakers when the weather is bad, who chatter in many languages and laugh a lot. The unoriginal thought occurs to me: one of you —why not that strapping African there?—might be a future pope.

They are students from the Pontifical Gregorian University nearby, who after morning classes hurry back to their colleges and convents for lunch. Many of them seem to have healthy appetites. A few say good-bye to women in conservative, casual clothes—nuns who don't wear their habits and female students who have attended the university lectures in Latin, Italian, English, French, German, and Spanish.

To its many hundreds of English-speaking students, the institution is the Greg. It is the Roman Catholic Church's Harvard, Princeton, and Yale, Oxford and Cambridge, Sorbonne and Al Azhar, all in one. Since its foundation by St. Ignatius of Loyola in 1551, the church's paramount center of higher learning has produced sixteen popes, hundreds of cardinals, and thousands of archbishops and bishops. Eight of its alumni have been canonized as saints.

When I first arrived in Rome many years ago, I was told to go to the Piazza della Pilotta—near where I live now but didn't then—at noontime any working day to watch a colorful spectactle. I followed the advice and saw compact groups of young scholars in varicolored priestly garb scurrying from the massive university building and briskly walking off in all directions, many in ranks of two or three like soldiers. There were ecclesiastics in violet cassocks with red sashes who, I learned, were Scotsmen, others in black cassocks with blue braid and red sashes who were Americans, and many others in variations of black, red, and blue. The gaudiest of them wore crimson, and many were blond and sturdy; they belonged to the German-Hungarian College, and because of their color the Romans called them the "crayfish," *gamberi*.

Some of this traditional seminarian attire can still be seen on rare ceremonial occasions when the Pope summons students to some function or when he visits one of their colleges. But for going to classes or moving around the city, the candidates for the priesthood and the postgraduate students of the Gregorian dress like students in secular institutions anywhere. The Pope's edicts on what priests and seminarians should wear in his own diocese—a long cassock, a Roman collar, a round hat, and, in winter, a dark cloak—just aren't heeded. Even many professors of the Gregorian University now prefer civilian clothes and neckties, with only a metal cross in their lapel to show they are clerics.

Discipline has eased in other respects. The vice-rector of one of the many colleges for seminarians tells me with some exasperation: "Our students come and go as they like. It's even surprising if they arrive in the refectory in time for dinner. We don't know what they do during the day—they think telling us robs them of their human rights. The next thing, they'll stay out overnight."

When the vice-rector was a student at the college he now helps to run, he needed a permit if he wanted to go off the institution's grounds, and if he did, he had to be accompanied by two other seminarians. He had to wear a cassock with many buttons all the time and wasn't allowed to enter the cell of a fellow student or admit one into his. He had to inform his "spiritual advisor," an older priest, of the books he intended to read. All classes at the Gregorian were in scholastic Latin, and there was no discussion or dialogue with teachers.

"I am now myself serving as spiritual advisor to our students," the vice-rector says. "But they tell *me* what I should read—Freud, Marxist and existentialist writers, Marcuse, Küng maybe, although I am of course familiar with most of that literature." The books by the "new theologians," such as Hans Küng, Edward Schillebeeckx, and others whose orthodoxy is questioned by the Vatican and by conservative churchmen at large, go from hand to hand among students at the Greg.

In a postgraduate seminar on modern intellectual trends that was conducted at the Gregorian University some time ago, Gore Vidal, the American author who lives in Italy, attended one of the weekly meetings as a guest speaker. The discussions were in English. Apparently meaning to shock the young priests, Vidal told them he didn't believe in God. The reaction by the audience was a politely bored "so what."

Not all of the three thousand students of the Gregorian University are quite so sophisticated, however. Many candidates for the priesthood, sent to Rome by bishops in the Third World, come sketchily prepared and have a hard time catching up with classmates from advanced countries and good schools. "Our university's standards have been revised upward and downward during the last two decades," a professor told me. "We have raised the intellectual ceiling and now have plenty of very smart students who are abreast of the scholarship in any of the great lay centers of learning throughout the world. And we had to lower the floor to high school level to take care of many seminarians from developing countries who otherwise would be unable to follow the courses."

It now takes the brightest students no less than seven years to earn a doctorate in theology at the Gregorian. By that time the scholar will long ago have been ordained to the priesthood, and he may be reasonably sure of going on to a teaching position or an auspicious church career in his home country or even in Rome. The elite of the Roman Catholic clergy is still to a large extent being trained at the Gregorian.

Yet, some years ago, archconservative bishops in the United States balked at the long-established practice of sending their most promising seminarians and young priests to the Gregorian University. The reason was distrust in the Jesuits who still dominate the faculty, and suspicion of their theology. Named after Pope Gregory XIII, a stern champion of the Catholic Counter-Reformation, the institution on the Piazza della Pilotta is still one of the most formidable power positions held by the Society of Jesus. But the image of the Jesuits, the largest religious order in the church, has gone through a remarkable change since the 1960s.

The mainstream within the Jesuit order seems to be flowing toward moderate liberalism. Echoing the misgivings of church conservatives, Pope John Paul II told the Jesuit leadership, in a tense audience during the first year of his pontificate, that he was worried about where the Jesuits were going. What's more, the pontiff publicly admonished the Very Reverend Pedro Arrupe, the Jesuit order's Spanish superior-general, that the order must halt liberal experiments.

"Of course, the Holy Father from Poland isn't an alumnus of the Greg," a Jesuit remarked to me ruefully. His two immediate predecessors, Pope Paul VI and Pope John Paul I, were. Karol Wojtyla, the young priest from Krakow who became the first non-Italian head of the church since the Renaissance, did his postgraduate studies right after the end of World War II at the Angelicum, the college of the Dominican Order. It is only a ten minutes' walk from the Gregorian and was at Wojtyla's time a citadel of orthodoxy.

The Angelicum is now known as the Pontifical University of St. Thomas Aquinas, and it is only one of more than thirty institutions in Rome that train priests in competition with

35

the Gregorian. But the Jesuit university is still in a class by itself owing to its international prestige and intellectual breadth.

For instance, some of the Greg's teachers and students doubtless know more about Marxism-Leninism than do most of the officials at the nearby headquarters of the Italian Communist Party. The Gregorian's Center of Marxist Studies is headed by an expert on Russian and Soviet philosophy, Prof. Gustav G. Wetter, who rates a substantial entry in the *Soviet Encyclopedia.* When I saw him last he told me that his center had been visited by a diplomat from the Soviet embassy in Rome, and that he and his colleagues were in touch with Soviet scholars and leaders of the Russian Orthodox Church in Moscow and Leningrad. "We aren't concerned with politics," he said. "We deal with ideas, philosophy, sociology, and literature."

A short, bearded Austrian, Father Wetter lives in a room at the university. On his shelves are the same books, periodicals, and newspapers that fill his Marxist center in the university's main building. Many other members of the Gregorian's faculty also have "cells"—which are often small studio apartments—near the classrooms. However, no students live on campus. Most of them belong to a diocese or a religious order and are put up in one of the more than two hundred satellite colleges maintained by their bishops or monastic groupings. The largest of them is the Pontifical North American College on the Janiculum Hill, with a postgraduate center in the Via dell' Umiltà, a stone's throw from the Greg.

Professors of the Gregorian University write books and travel far and wide, attending scholarly congresses or participating in scientific projects in distant places. The Pontifical Bible Institute, an annex to the Gregorian, sends select graduate students to Hebrew University in Jerusalem for language training and research in scriptural disciplines in a Rome-Jerusalem Biblical Project. ("St. Jerome studied

36

Hebrew in the fourth century under the rabbis of Bethlehem," a Jesuit comments.)

The Bible Institute is housed in two older buildings in the square, the Piazza della Pilotta, on which frowns the facade of the Gregorian's main structure. The principal element of the papal university complex went up in the late 1920s. Its neo-baroque heaviness was the church's unfortunate reply to the contemporary Mussolini-modern style; other ecclesiastical buildings erected in that period inside the Vatican and in other parts of Rome are in the same sullen and graceless mode. The Holy See had just received large funds from Mussolini's government as part of the accords—the Lateran Treaties of 1929—that created the State of Vatican City. Pope Pius XI at once launched a building program. One good thing can be said about his architects: they built solidly. The Gregorian University, like other church structures inaugurated in the early 1930s, has stood up well to the passage of time. Many of the buildings Mussolini commissioned already look decrepit.

The fourth, or north, side of the Piazza della Pilotta is occupied by a stately old building, the Palazzo Frascara, which now houses classrooms, seminars, and comfortable cells for Jesuit professors. The Gregorian University's structures and the square that they enclose form an academic quadrangle where students and teachers stroll and neighborhood business owners and residents, like me, park their cars. It is characteristic of our cozy town-gown relations that we know a lot of what is going on behind the walls of the pontifical university.

The neighbors chuckled when they heard of the American Jesuit teacher who asked his superior if he could break the rules by locking the door to his cell in one of the buildings on the quadrangle. It seems that a fellow priest from Latin America, overwrought and under the illusion that the American had struck a deal with Satan, had intruded and threatened to kill him.

And then there was the Spanish Jesuit sociologist who wrote a slim booklet on his spiritual and moral travails that everybody wanted to read. The Spaniard disclosed that he had managed to keep his priestly obligation of celibacy only because he had resorted to masturbation. It may have been the first time that a cleric, and a Jesuit at that, had made such a confession in print.

It would nevertheless be wrong to conclude from such anecdotes that there is a flood of gossip about the Gregorian University or the church's academic establishment in Rome in general. There isn't. Although the Greg has gone coeducational, with nuns and laywomen attending classes in theology and canon law side by side with seminarians, and despite the new permissiveness in attire and discipline, few of the candidates for the priesthood and the priestly postgraduates seem to get into trouble.

The hundreds of professors and thousands of students of the church universities and colleges in Rome walk daily past the pornographic displays on newsstands and cinema marquees, cannot ignore the streetwalkers and drug peddlers, see the scantily dressed woman tourists, and breathe the ripe atmosphere of the sensual and cynical city that is all around them. However, the quadrangle is a different Rome, where no scandals seem to occur. It is an enclave and a community whose members speak many languages, get up early to work on doctoral dissertations, and follow events in faraway countries. Now and then, of course, they too slip around the corner to an espresso bar for a quick *cappuccino* or an ice cream.

"PLAY THE WHORE"

Elsa has been in the business for at least thirty years, if not longer. Despite her girlish ways with clients, especially new ones, she is unmistakably a veteran. Her address—near the Piazza Barberini, one of the busiest spots in central Rome—and her phone number are listed every working day in the "Massage" ads of *Il Messaggero,* and anyone who goes carefully through its classified pages will also find Elsa's phone number, though no address, in the section called "Professional Activities." There, the text reads: "Girl student, Art School, available for public relations. Call for appointment."

Elsa's place of work is an old house without a doorman. As in many residential buildings all over the city, the entrance door is usually closed, and visitors have to use an intercom to ask occupants of apartments for admittance. The system is called the *citofono.* In the streets of Rome, one can often observe people conducting long dialogues with a voice out of the *citofono* before the building door opens; sometimes it doesn't, and the people go away. Not at Elsa's, though; she is running a hospitable place.

Those who press the button corresponding to the apartment number given in the *Il Messaggero* ad don't have to identify themselves. The door at once unlocks electrically. Elsa's apartment door on the second floor carries only a number, no nameplate. This is not so unusual: anonymity prevails throughout the building, although one door does carry the sign of an import-export company.

For many years Elsa has owned the apartment in her

39

condominium building. The other people living or working there have obviously become used to the coming and going of her visitors all day long, or maybe they themselves are leading busy lives. Elsa receives from ten A.M. without any lunch break and goes home around seven P.M., but she doesn't say where home is.

When Elsa's doorbell rings, she looks through a peephole before opening. A caller sees very little at first, because her hall is only dimly lit by a red lightbulb. She is sometimes a blonde, sometimes dark-haired, wearing various wigs and low-cut dresses. Many clients, old and new, quickly pay what amounts to between $12 and $23, the charges for most of her services. They are taken to one of three rooms in the apartment, and they don't stay very long. Sometimes a visitor has to wait and is shown into a room with stacks of old pornographic magazines and pinups on the walls.

Quite often a newcomer will balk after his eyes adjust to the red light and he realizes that his hostess must be at least in her fifties. Then Elsa, by no means offended, puts on a mysterious look and whispers: "I have something special for you—a very young girl friend of mine who just happens to be visiting me. She is so sweet. But you'll have to pay her 100,000 lire." The amount is equal to $110. In other words, Elsa is also a procuress. She has a bevy of young women "friends," most of them in their early twenties, whose attentions may be booked by phone. They also take turns with clients who aren't eager for Elsa's cut-rate ministrations and can pay more.

What the young women earn on the premises is evenly split with Elsa. A few visitors who are especially appreciative of the "public relations" they have just experienced give the young practitioners a little more money than they had been promised, but Elsa seems to have a way of learning about such largess, and insists on her 50 percent share of it. She detests any direct arrangements between her young "friends" and their clients. Sometimes one of the women gives her own phone number to a client. If Elsa finds out about such a violation of the unwritten house rules, she throws the offender out and henceforth bars her from the circuit.

None of Elsa's young women friends is really a student at art school or any other institution. One of them is occasionally seen selling jeans and mod shirts in one of the garishly lit casual-wear shops that have recently sprung up downtown. Another member of Elsa's stable, who claims she is nineteen years old and probably isn't more than twenty-four, says she tells her mother she has a part-time job with a lawyer. "I won't do this forever," she remarks. "I just need the money now."

All the young women at Elsa's, some of them quite attractive, seem to know one another. Occasionally they introduce a new candidate for "public relations" to their den mother.

Now and then Elsa has a glass of brandy with an old client. "This is no bordello," she will observe. "This is a high-class place. Important people from the ministries, priests, army officers come here. My friends are nice, well-behaved girls, and I try to help them. No pimp comes near us." Does she ever have any trouble with the police? "Why should I? Never."

Romans who have known Elsa for years and are familiar with how their city functions are convinced that she has influential protectors and must be paying them off. This appears to be true of many of the women, and some men, who are regularly listed in the "Massage" and "Professional Activities" advertisements.

Prostitution has flourished in Rome without any major interruption since antiquity, at times quite openly, but always tacitly tolerated. It is at present neither legal nor illegal. Under current legislation, the exploitation of prostitutes and soliciting in the streets are punishable offenses, and the police are no longer permitted to card-index known prostitutes as they once did. It is nevertheless known that files on members of the milieu are being kept. The police justify this practice with the contention that sex for sale breeds crime.

The present prostitution laws date from 1958, the year the licensed "houses of tolerance" were closed. Some old Romans speak with undisguised nostalgia of their visits to those bordellos. The more expensive ones were in the Via degli Avignonesi, the Via Capo Le Case, the Via della Fontanella, and other central streets. Most of these establishments have been transformed into small hotels; few of today's guests know about the bawdy history of their austerely furnished rooms and whitewashed lobbies. Cheaper licensed brothels did roaring business near the army barracks and the central railroad terminal. One person who can't forget their raucous atmosphere is Federico Fellini, as his films attest.

Until 1958, the women in the "houses of tolerance" used to stay for two weeks in one place, then move to some other bordello in Rome or in the provinces. Madams were wealthy personages with good connections at police headquarters and even higher up. They kept one another informed on the earning power and discipline of each of their "girls." Prostitutes were card-indexed by the police like mafiosi or people with criminal records. They had to be examined at regular intervals by officially appointed physicians, and their civil rights were curtailed in many ways. Among other things, they were denied the police certificate of good behavior that Italians need for applications to some jobs and for various dealings with the authorities. Bordello operators were heavily taxed and, in addition, had to make contributions to the notorious "black funds" of the police, which were used to pay informers and to finance other unaccountable activities.

The women in a licensed brothel normally kept 50 percent of their earnings and turned over the other half to the madam. They were charged for meals, other in-house services, and the periodic visits by the doctor. Nevertheless, women who weren't additionally exploited by a pimp were able to save a lot of money. Elsa's friends believe she was one of them, and thus could easily afford to buy the apartment she works in, and probably also her hideaway home.

The system of the "houses of tolerance" in effect made the

government a partner of the madams in managing prostitution and skimming money off it. In 1951, a Socialist member of Parliament and former schoolteacher, Lina Merlin, introduced a draft bill to outlaw the licensed bordellos. (In France, Marthe Richard had started a successful antibrothel crusade years earlier.) It took the Italian Chamber of Deputies and the Senate seven years to pass the "Merlin Law." On September 20, 1958, six months after it went into force, the last "houses of tolerance" closed down, inspiring a stream of maudlin end-of-an-era prose in newspapers and magazines.

With the demise of the licensed bordellos, prostitution poured into the streets of Rome with a vengeance. Fifteen years later, an Italian League for the Defense of Prostitutes, which was to prove short-lived, estimated at a press conference that at least ten thousand streetwalkers were plying their trade in the city every day. This army of women was complemented by battalions of male prostitutes and a flashy train of pimps in Jaguars and Porsches.

At the same time, semiclandestine call houses began to proliferate, flimsily masquerading as massage or beauty parlors, language schools, fashion shops, and escort services. From time to time the police would raid such a place, take the identities of the women and clients found on the premises, and arrest the manager on charges of exploiting prostitution. But many other such businesses, including Elsa's, have continued to function undisturbed despite their daily publicity in the press. Experts believe that several thousand women are currently engaged, full-time or part-time, in off-street prostitution in Rome.

Police officers say that racketeers control most of the streetwalkers and call girl rings, and that the sex trade is a major cause of the present surge in crime. In one bizarre case, four hardy young women who habitually hung out on a stretch of the Raccordo Anulare, the circular motor road on the far outskirts of Rome that links the thruways, were arrested and charged with having robbed and blackmailed many truck drivers. When the victims turned on the four, the women allegedly threatened to tell everything to the wives whose addresses they had learned from identity cards and driver's licenses in the stolen wallets. The all-woman gang was reportedly smashed when a widowed trucker proved impervious to the threats and informed the police.

In winter, prostitutes on the beltway enclosing Rome and in other outlying spots light bonfires to keep warm while they wait for clients to drive up in trucks or cars. The slang word for what in America is called the john is *pollo,* chicken, the implication being that the woman's job is to pluck the fowl. A prostitute who get into a chicken's auto to drive off to some lover's lane or maybe to his home is often followed by her pimp in a racing car or on a powerful motorcycle as protection against being robbed and as a standby in case of some other emergency. In Roman idiom the innocuous-sounding word *protettore,* protector, has taken on the meaning "pimp."

Several neighborhoods in the suburbs and in the center of Rome swarm with streetwalkers most of the day, especially in the evening. Notorious beats for prostitutes of both sexes are the Tor di Quinto district on the northern approaches to the Tiber River and the Tiber embankments in the northern part of the city, the archeological zone from the Baths of Caracalla to the Circus Maximus, the nearby Colosseum area—a place of ill repute even in imperial Rome—and the central railroad terminal and its environs. Many of the women loiterers around the railroad terminal are Africans. Most of them came from the former Italian colonies of Eritrea, Somalia, and Ethiopia to work in domestic service jobs, and were then persuaded by local pimps of both sexes to change their calling.

Vice squad agents say that the professional prostitutes whom they know well complain vocally about new competition from very young women outside the milieu. "With thousands of teenage drug addicts in the city now," a police officer explained, "a girl will solicit to get the money for a fix. But that isn't all. A group of high school kids will stay away from classes and go to have fun in the Villa Borghese gardens or the World Fair district. The boys will have no money for cigarettes or for filling up their motor scooters. One of them will say to the girls, half in joke, 'Why don't you play the whore and ask some old guy in a car for a ride?' Some nice-looking chick will take the dare, and after half an hour she'll be back with enough money to buy cigarettes and fuel, plus pizza, soft drinks, and ice cream for everyone."

The most expensive streetwalkers are to be found in the Via Veneto from late afternoon into the night. They wait to be picked up by foreigners or visiting businessmen from northern Italy. A few of these women offer to take their clients to cozy apartments and pour them drinks. Others have deals with nearby hotels. Racketeers rigidly control the Via Veneto turf and assign zones of operation—so many feet of sidewalk—to the women they "protect."

Most of the Via Veneto streetwalkers double as call girls, at an even higher rate, whenever a middleman in one of the luxury hotels has an impatient guest on his hands. Hotel employes and escort services also have the phone numbers of many other women who are ready to keep company with moneyed patrons.

Today, Arabs with millions of lire to spend during a brief stay in the Italian capital are particularly welcome. A former impresario who used to organize variety shows and beauty contests is now making plenty of money from Arab guests entrusted to him by business organizations. "My charges aren't any big sheiks," he says. "Those go to Paris, Monte Carlo, London, and New York to have fun. The second-string Arabs that we get are officials, businessmen, diplomats. They too have a lot of money and don't mind spending a couple of thousand dollars for an evening if it's worth their while. Quite a few of them have asked some girl they have met through me to accompany them back to the Middle East, and have made them big promises. No girl has gone, as far as I know."

45

Elsa says she has no Arab clients and sees few foreigners. Between frequent phone calls she explains: "I have enough to do with Italians. Young ones, old ones. Most of them don't say who they are, but they don't fool me. Sometimes I see their picture in the newspaper or recognize them on television. You'd be surprised. Some come here regularly, others whenever they have a fight with their wife or girl friend and need a woman to tell all about it. I can't go on vacation. I just take Sundays off," she says.

Elsa's place is also closed on Good Friday, on the feast of the Assumption of the Virgin Mary, August 15, and from Christmas Eve to December 26. When the pastor of the parish church comes during Holy Week to bless the apartments and businesses in the building, as priests do all over Rome before Easter, Elsa demurely receives him in the hallway, asks him to sprinkle holy water in the direction of her three rooms, and gives him a big contribution for his charities. "I wouldn't miss the Easter benediction for anything in the world," she says. "But I don't let the priest go beyond the hall."

THE TERRACE

To his relatives, who seem to have multiplied since he became rich, he is Uncle Annibale. He is generous to nephews and nieces, cordial to their parents, and friendly to other members of the clan who have recently taken to calling him "uncle." Whenever there is a wedding in the family, he sends lavish gifts, and he will gladly become a godfather to the babies who arrive later. Remote cousins turn to Uncle Annibale when they have a son or daughter to "systemize," possibly in a government job. He usually is able to help.

Once a year, Uncle Annibale throws a party for his relatives at his villa near Marino in the hills southeast of Rome. On a long table on the terrace there are pâté de foie gras, smoked salmon, Parma ham and other delicacies, fine pastry and ice cream, plenty to drink. Uncle Annibale and his wife —they are childless—try to put their guests, most of them simple people, at their ease.

At one of his annual family gatherings, Uncle Annibale couldn't refrain from confiding to a group of relatives, "Would you believe that the arrangement for the new government was practically made on this terrace?" The remark was a mistake; during the following days Uncle Annibale received far more than the usual number of phone calls from favor seekers.

But Uncle Annibale's boast about history made on his terrace was basically accurate. Leaders of the parties that were to set up a new government coalition had met at a dinner party in his villa and had discussed who would get the treasury and who would become foreign minister. Completely unknown to newspaper readers and Italians at large, over the last few years Uncle Annibale has become something of a power broker. His villa and, when the weather is good, its terrace, are essential to the way he operates.

Uncle Annibale and his wife are tireless party givers. Several times a week they have influential guests for lunch or dinner in either large or intimate groups. Government members, politicians of various denominations, high officials, magistrates, prelates of the church, business magnates, and top officers of the armed forces have sat at their table. It takes just forty-five minutes to get out to Marino by car from, say, the Chamber of Deputies or the head office of one of the big banks. Characteristically, Uncle Annibale always sees to it that the drivers who bring his guests are also well fed.

Uncle Annibale never asks any relatives to these affairs. Journalists are always barred, and the Italian press hasn't yet found out about his parties. The cuisine is justly famous. A woman from the Venice region is in command of the kitchen; her husband serves as butler and oversees other personnel. Uncle Annibale's obscure brothers and sisters-in-law have figured out that the household staff alone must cost him a small fortune.

But the main attraction of Uncle Annibale's villa and its terrace is privacy. Rome isn't a city where prominent people can easily meet without everybody knowing about it. In Uncle Annibale's villa, politicos who attack each other in Parliament, high-ranking bureaucrats, executives of big business corporations, and a few diplomats have spun some of the cabals that are the essence of Roman power plays. Uncle Annibale and his wife know when they have to leave guests alone, maybe in a corner of the terrace, with only the butler hovering nearby, keeping them supplied with coffee, brandy, and cigars.

Where Uncle Annibale has acquired his undeniable flair for bringing important people together is even more of a mystery than are the sources of his wealth. One of several sons of a railroad employee, he started out as a traveling salesman for a textile firm. He must have landed big clients, for in a few years he was head of the company's marketing department. He still sells textiles—thousands of bed sheets for hospitals, miles of fabric for police and military uniforms. He also mediates public works contracts and is said to have pulled off million-dollar deals with the state-controlled industries.

Where is Uncle Annibale going from here? He may be tempted to accept the presidency of one of the large semigovernmental agencies or the directorship of a bank. Perhaps the newspapers will catch up with his parties, and photographers will swarm outside the villa, scaring off guests. Or, much worse, some new scandal may boil up and Uncle Annibale may somehow get blistered by it.

"Look at what happened to the Caltagirones," one of Uncle Annibale's cousins told a friend. Gaetano Caltagirone and his two brothers had been among the biggest contractors in Rome, controlling more than a hundred overlapping real estate companies. The three Sicilian brothers had no trouble obtaining easy loans from government-controlled credit institutions, and they built thousands of apartments. Gaetano Caltagirone's sumptuous villa on Monte Mario, which also had a large terrace, saw many parties. When the president of the republic made him a Knight of Work, Italy's highest official honor for successful businessmen, Gaetano gave a reception at his villa that was newsworthy for its assemblage of Rome's political-bureaucratic establishment.

The prime ministers, political leaders, prestigious officials, artists, and beautiful women who attended Gaetano Caltagirone's parties were treated to caviar, spaghetti, and champagne. The photographers ate and drank well, too, as they shot pictures of the Sicilian entrepreneur flanked by prominent guests.

When the Caltagirone empire suddenly collapsed like a circus tent hit by a tornado, newspapers pulled the photos out of their files and published them. As they also reported, the companies of the Sicilian trio were without cash and had to halt their half-finished construction projects. The fiscal authorities demanded payment of enormous tax arrears. The judiciary brought bankruptcy charges against the three brothers and issued arrest warrants alleging fraud. The Caltagirones were found to have surreptitiously left Italy. Gaetano Caltagirone arrived in New York in his own executive jet and announced that he wanted to start a contracting business in the United States. Italy obtained his and a brother's arrest in New York; the third Caltagirone brother was picked up in Santo Domingo.

The scandal engulfed a government member, Merchant Navy Minister Franco Evangelisti. The minister, who liked to speak in broad Roman dialect, admitted in a published interview that he had taken money gifts from his friend, Gaetano Caltagirone, as had, he asserted, many other politicians. Whenever he met the rich contractor, the minister said candidly, Gaetano would take his checkbook out of his pocket and ask, "Fra', what do you need?" (Fra' is idiomatic Roman for Franco.) The minister insisted that the funds he had received from Caltagirone had been used for political purposes, and that he had never done any favors in return. The "Fra', what do you need?" became proverbial. Evangelisti was forced to resign from the government, and the scandal widened.

The political organization for which he said he had accepted the Sicilian's money was headed by former Prime Minister Giulio Andreotti, for many years one of Italy's most powerful personages. The beached minister of the merchant navy, who at one time had served as president of the Roma soccer club, had long been Andreotti's chief lieutenant in a faction within the Christian Democratic Party.

Since the end of Mussolini's dictatorship, the Christian Democrats have been Italy's strongest political machine; they always have controlled the central government in Rome. Backed, though with varying intensity, by the Vatican and most of the country's Roman Catholic clergy, the

Christian Democrats really aren't a movement but a conservative state of mind and a coalition of disparate groups. The factions feud with one another, split, change names, realign, rally into a common front just before every election, and start quarreling again afterward, at all times jockeying for power. For decades the Andreotti-Evangelisti faction had been able to dispense much patronage—jobs, pensions for imaginary victims of World War II, and the like. The Caltagirone scandal ended all that.

The disgrace of the Caltagirone brothers also made the opulent place on Monte Mario somewhat disreputable; nobody in the Roman establishment today wants to be reminded of ever having been there.

The Italian capital isn't a clubby city. The rich and powerful, many members of the educated middle class, and above all the young people keep complaining that there are few chances to make new social contacts. The old Golf Club is one place that has always sheltered an exclusive coterie. Aristocrats, some wealthy people who have lived abroad, diplomats, and English-speaking prelates from the Vatican can be found at the splendid golf course, swimming pool, and restaurant on rolling land between the ancient and new Appian ways. The place is called by a very Roman name, Acqua Santa, or Holy Water. In the declining years of the Fascist regime, the club provided the setting for the dalliances of Count Galeazzo Ciano, Mussolini's frivolous son-in-law and foreign minister, with Roman princesses. Now, the Acqua Santa golf course, besieged by housing developments that are marching in from various directions, is an enclave that has little to do with present-day Rome.

The Chess Club and the Hunting Club are opulently housed in downtown Rome, three blocks from each other. The membership of both is replete with aged and visibly bored noblemen who drop in to read the newspapers, gossip, and play cards. Both clubs have liveried footmen who also look bored, and dining rooms where indifferent meals are served. The prestige of the two places has declined over the years as the influence of the aristocracy has waned. Visiting foreign notables are still sometimes entertained by Italian diplomats in one of the two anemic clubs, and are expected to be impressed when the staff greet their host as "prince" or "marquess." Social climbers may still aspire to join them and still suffer traumas when snobbish cliques blackball them. (During the first postwar years, an ambitious American committed suicide after his application for membership in the Hunting Club was turned down.) However, little of consequence takes place on the gilded premises, which look a little shabbier every year.

The Roma and the Lazio soccer factions take care of thousands of Romans who feel the need for tribal togetherness. A few other clubs professing sporting or regional interests are mostly fronts for gambling. There was also an upstart "Lodge P. 2" (the abbreviation stands for "Masonic Propaganda No. 2") operating outside the mainstream of Freemasonry. It was a clandestine financial and political mutual-help organization active in the late 1970s and early 1980s. It was a shadowy network of influential personages with right-wing leanings founded by a businessman from Tuscany, Licio Gelli. Some of its nearly two thousand secret members sometimes turned up unobtrusively at Uncle Annibale's dinner parties.

A little livelier, and at the center of Rome's social stage, are salons that bring political and business figures together with artists, members of the intelligentsia, and sometimes beautiful women. Leading Christian Democrats, Socialists, and politicos of minor parties often turn up, but ranking Communists rarely accept invitations. Members of the Communist Party hierarchy may, however, occasionally consent to meet with "bourgeois" politicians and capitalist tycoons in an out-of-sight place like Uncle Annibale's terrace.

At a dinner party given recently by an ambitious dowager who must remain unnamed, there were several members of Parliament, various well-known journalists, an industrial leader from northern Italy, and two young women who looked like fashion models. The conversation was predictable. The guests started speaking about movies the young women had just seen, then moved to the breakup of a noted playboy's marriage, soccer, and the latest financial-political scandal.

It was talk of the kind that drags on in any trattoria at night when diners are laboriously digesting the heavy food they have eaten and procrastinating about going home. Rome has grown and become wealthier, says Alberto Moravia, the novelist, but "it has remained tied to an idea of elementary and coarse living—this absence of refinement is being felt everywhere." Moravia, a native Roman, adds, "The city, thus, is very vulgar." He wasn't among the guests in the dowager's salon, but if he had been there, he would not have changed his judgment.

Complaints about how provincial Roman society is and how unsophisticated its conversation and entertainments are can often be heard at diplomatic affairs when no local guest is within earshot. Nevertheless, foreign ambassadors and their principal aides work hard to have a cross section of influential and knowledgeable Italians at their table so as to sound them out on what is going on behind the scenes. A small luncheon offered by the French ambassador in the magnificent Renaissance Palazzo Farnese may be far more informative and stimulating than a week of meals at the Hunting Club or parties in the now fashionable salons around the Spanish Square.

But for both significance and privacy, there is little in Rome to compare with the gatherings on Uncle Annibale's terrace. I know of nowhere else where the power elite can meet, relax, and talk about deals without journalists and cameramen around and without fear of terrorists. In the future, his terrace may become even more important than it has been in the past—until a new party giver with the same remarkable political savvy comes to the fore.

TRUTH IN THE
TRATTORIA

As the new year got under way, Romans who eat out were confronted with an unsettling novelty. When they asked for the check, they were now supposed to receive the copy of a form detailing each course and beverage, including taxes due. The blanks used for the operation had to be previously stamped and numbered by the fiscal authorities.

What's more, restaurant patrons were warned to keep the checks because inspectors might be hovering outside eating places and request proof that the regulations were being observed. Plainclothesmen of the Finance Guard might pose as guests, eat lunches or dinners, and then proceed with spot checks.

Many people had the uneasy feeling that official snoopers were invading a hitherto inviolate piece of their personal life, almost as if they were asked after a romantic encounter to make a formal statement on what exactly had happened. The authorities felt the need to assure patrons that their names wouldn't have to be on restaurant checks. But a diner who couldn't furnish proof of having requested a "fiscal receipt" might have to pay a fine exceeding the price of the meal.

The new rules were meant to curb tax dodging in the catering business, which officials estimated had so far concealed up to 70 percent of the turnover. Many residents, however, worried that the fiscal innovation might deal a crippling blow to one of the few institutions that till then had functioned admirably—the trattoria.

Franco Romagnoli, who runs the Antica Trattoria Al Moro, announced, rather glumly, that the reform "will make no difference, our prices stay unchanged." The Moro, or Moor, four dining rooms on a narrow street between the Corso and the Trevi Fountain, is popular with artists and with members of Parliament who walk over from the nearby Chamber of Deputies.

The specialty of the house is spaghetti *alla Moro,* extremely *al dente* and garnished with small chunks of bacon. From a wall, a grave face with heavy pouches under the eyes scowls on patrons. It's a blown-up still from Fellini's *Satyricon* of the owner's father, Mario Romagnoli, who had a part in the movie. The film director from the Romagna region was a frequent guest at the Moro when the older Romagnoli was still in charge, and he talked the restaurateur into joining the cast. Over the years, Fellini assembled many of his films' extraordinary characters in this way.

Now the older Romagnoli is ailing and stays at home, and his son has a long working day. I often see him in the morning at our neighborhood market, with the ramparts of the Quirinal Palace as a backdrop, pinching tomatoes to feel whether they are firm and seeking out the season's fruit. The tall, dark restaurant manager with his red neckerchief is also a familiar figure at the sprawling outdoor market in the Trionfale section near the Vatican, which is renowned for its wide choice of farm produce and its moderate prices.

Shortly after the new regulation was imposed, the younger Romagnoli appeared on television together with fellow leaders of Rome's four thousand restaurateurs to explain why they had decided to close down their businesses for a day in protest against the "fiscal receipt." "We are caterers who want to provide good meals for our patrons in a pleasant ambiance; we aren't accountants" was the argument of the trattoria owners. "Why pick on us? Why not tighten fiscal controls on physicians and dentists or, for that matter, on plumbers, who are all known to accept only cash and often refuse to issue receipts?"

The finance minister replied that the authorities would soon get around to checking up on professional people and highly paid craftsmen; meanwhile, a start in the fight against tax evasion must be made somewhere.

On the day the restaurateurs picked for locking out their guests, most sit-down eating places did remain shut, but hungry Romans were able to eat sandwiches at espresso bars, which stayed open. The waiters' unions supported the government's tax reform. Eventually, the trattoria industry called off a second scheduled shutdown and decided to negotiate with the finance minister. One concession the restaurateurs obtained was that the stiff penalties for noncompliance with the new fiscal rules would be fully enforced only at the end of the year.

The spokesmen for the trattoria trade told the minister that many places were being victimized by protection rackets. Two or three burly men would march into some restaurant, order and eat a hearty meal, and then coldly announce they weren't paying. If the manager said he was going to call the police, the freeloaders would mirthlessly explain that it was all a joke, but there would be trouble in the next few days —windows might be smashed or guests harassed, a bomb might go off during the night. The same things, and worse, might happen if restaurateurs refused money demands from gangsters.

The authorities conceded that the catering industry had some expenses for which it couldn't account, and granted them a flat 10 percent exemption from their total turnover. This was to cover the required expense of keeping records on all the meat, pasta, vegetables, wine, and other supplies the trattorias buy and what they pay for them, as well as the bookkeeping involved in computing salaries, cost-of-living bonuses, and social security contributions for waiters and kitchen help.

Still, it is no secret that all these records kept by a trattoria reflect only a part of reality (as is the situation in most other businesses). I know an eating place in the Trastevere district where the chef is an Algerian and his two kitchen assistants are Tunisians; none of them exist for the authorities—they are illegal immigrants who are paid below union scale, evade income tax, and lack social security coverage.

Many other restaurant workers connive with their employers to report only a part of their earnings. The law expects waiters to account for tips, but they do so only minimally. "Most foreigners now ask if service is included in the check, and of course we have to say yes, and then they leave no tip at all," said a waiter at a trattoria-pizzeria near the *Il Messaggero* newspaper building. "Our Roman patrons once used to leave a tip amounting to about 10 percent of the sum on the check; now less than 5 percent is the rule."

There are no such accounting and tipping problems in the few mom-and-pop places that have survived. One, which I visit fairly often, is on a small side street behind the Borghese Gardens, rather distant from the center of the city, where I live, but worth the twenty-minute bus trip. Mother works alone in the kitchen, turning out pasta in almost any style and three or four main courses for lunch and dinner six days a week. Father does most of the shopping and serves at tables. A grown-up daughter helps out as a waitress during the lunchtime rush. In the evening, her fiancé, who has another job, often turns up to lend a hand.

The fare is simple and robust; the white wine from the Adriatic coast is drinkable. A satisfying, plain meal may cost five dollars, and habitués pay even less. The tablecloths are always white and clean, and each patron gets a freshly laundered, often still slightly damp, white napkin. (Paper napkins are only used in espresso bars, stand-up eating places, and cafeterias.)

The small sign outside says just OSTERIA. Once, the word designated the plainest eating places, far less elaborate than a trattoria or a *ristorante.* In recent years some establishments, affecting a measure of sophistication by

57

understatement, have reverted to the old name, as if winking at people with old-fashioned tastes and a yearning for mother's home cooking. The term is frequently, and pretentiously, spelled "hostaria," an archaic form as suspect as "ye olde shoppe."

Rome now has a few Chinese, Japanese, and Vietnamese restaurants, but there has been nothing comparable to the recent invasion of Asian cuisine in other big European cities or in the United States. There are far fewer French restaurants in Rome than Italian ones in Paris. Among the three or four I know, L'Eau Vive is the most unusual because it is run by a Belgian-based nuns' order in an old palazzo near the Pantheon. Young sisters of the community, wearing secular dress, serve at tables, and by the time most guests are through with dinner, they sing a religious hymn. Not surprisingly, many priests and Christian Democratic politicians fancy the place.

What else is there in the way of exotic eating-out in Rome? A North African restaurant near the Vatican featuring couscous, a few Germanic beer houses, a Hungarian goulash-and-gypsy cellar, a couple of Greek taverns where one can sample resin-flavored wine, and that's about all.

The fact is, the overwhelming majority of Romans are only too happy to leave the foreign restaurants to foreigners—diplomats, expatriates, and tourists. Italians in general expect a meal to consist of pasta, meat or fish, plenty of fresh vegetables, and fruit or dessert. Eating habits don't change from the Alps to Sicily; they are a unifying force, like the espresso addiction, in a nation that more than a century after achieving political unity is still torn by deep cultural differences. Within the hallowed three-course canon, however, there are certain regional variations—in northeastern Italy, cornmeal mush (polenta) is often substituted for pasta, and Naples has contributed the pizza. In the capital, regional cooking is well represented by many Venetian, Bolognese, Tuscan, and Neapolitan restaurants. A Sicilian place is mockingly called Il Mafioso.

As in Paris and other culinary shrines around the world, it is possible to get a bad restaurant meal in Rome. Tourists are often served overcooked spaghetti, tough meat, dubious sauces, limp salad, sulfurous wine, and maybe even a demitasse tasting like dishwater in the cute places to which they are steered by travel bureaus and coach operators. Old-timers here swear that a few months after a respectable trattoria is listed for the first time in one of the popular tourist guidebooks, the quality of the food and wine deteriorates while prices go up. On the whole, it is better to stay away from places where the decor is overly contrived. I will often walk into some trattoria with whitewashed walls and few visible frills where a local clientele seems to prevail. The name may be Da Nino, or L'Abruzzese. The manager, puzzled by a new face, will try to cut a good figure, *fare buona figura.*

In many years of eating out in Rome I can hardly remember being served by a surly waiter. After months or years of exposure to sullen, sloppy, incompetent, or outright rude service in New York, Eastern Europe, and the Third World, it has always been a joy to come back to a Roman trattoria. The food may not be on a par with top French cuisine, and one will have to settle for a less than great wine, but neither will the patron encounter the kind of hauteur displayed by many French maîtres d'hôtel or sommeliers. In a city ruled by ponderous church and civil bureaucracies where it seems so much more fatiguing to get things done than in any other center of the industrial world, restaurants as a rule are marvels of efficiency, speed, quality, and courtesy.

May it be noted in this paean to Roman trattoria managers and their staffs that they are usually helpful to foreigners, patient with them when they speak not a word of Italian or say they want no wine; they try to feed them well and also to provide entertainment by clowning a little. In most of the dozen or so places that I prefer, the same waiters have been around for years, some of them for many years. They deal with regular guests in a familiar way that is equally distant from servility and arrogance.

The genial efficiency of Roman restaurants spills over to their patrons. Business is often done over lunch or dinner. Politicians of opposing parties, table-hopping in some crowded trattoria near the Chamber of Deputies or the Senate, may lay the groundwork for a deal. Gianni Agnelli, the head of the Fiat motor empire and one of the richest and most powerful Italians, seen having lunch with foreign guests at the El Toulà restaurant near the Palazzo Borghese, may be discussing a joint venture running into millions of dollars.

Much of what passes for social life in Rome also takes place in the trattoria. I have several friends who have never asked me to their homes and don't expect me to invite them to mine. But we often meet in a restaurant. Every now and then, one or the other of them may suggest I meet him and the woman in his life for dinner at their favorite trattoria, where we will linger over wine for hours after the meal, talking, talking.

When the tax reform was new, we talked a lot about the future of the Roman trattoria. If truthfulness in restaurant checks and bookkeeping were rigorously enforced, pessimists warned, prices would rise prohibitively, the quality of food and service would decline, and many eating establishments would have to close down.

But cynics, always the majority in Rome, predicted that the trattoria industry would speedily work out the "arrangement" necessary for a triumphant survival. And, as usual, the cynics proved to be right. During the months following the trattoria reform, a two-tier system evolved whereby some guests were given the newfangled checks and others weren't. "Do you want a fiscal receipt?" headwaiters in many places now ask routinely. Diners who connive at tax evasion say they don't want it, in the hope of paying less. There is, of course, a remote chance that a fiscal inspector may ambush them outside, but they can always try to convince him they have just dropped in to look for a friend without eating anything, or that somebody who left earlier has paid for them. The thrill of outwitting the tax people adds to the pleasure of the trattoria. Working out an "arrangement" is, after all, a Roman way of life.

LIFE AS ARRANGEMENT

Cars that have no business being in downtown Rome are now barred from the historical center. City hall's sound idea was to allow only public buses, taxis, ambulances, the official dark blue limousines of the government, and the vehicles of actual residents of the area into the narrow streets and stage-like squares between the Porta del Popolo and the Piazza Venezia, the Villa Borghese and the Tiber River.

I was therefore surprised, though only to a degree, when I saw Eduardo get out of an Alfa Romeo that he had nonchalantly double-parked on the Piazza di Spagna. The car carried on its windshield a city sign in red and yellow—Rome's colors—authorizing it to circulate freely within the restricted zone.

How did he get the coveted sign, I asked him. Did he now live in the center? *"Mi sono arrangiato,"* Eduardo said with a wink. His reply would translate literally as "I have arranged myself." The true meaning is: I managed with the means at hand; I used my wits and made do.

Eduardo may have rendered a small service to a city bureaucrat or a police officer in exchange for the car sign; he may have lifted it from another automobile; or he may have bought it from one of the small printshops that, on the side, forge official permits and credentials. However he managed it, it is further evidence that Eduardo is a virtuoso of the "arrangement," the cherished Roman way of tackling adversity, coasting along, coping with life's problems, and surviving by one's wits. And he isn't even a native of the city.

Calling on Eduardo's services from time to time over the years, or taking an espresso and chatting with him for a few minutes during chance encounters, I have pieced together his story. He came to Rome from one of the poor, crowded towns near Naples. He had never finished school, and had just been discharged from the army, where his natural talent for arrangement had landed him a cushy job in the officers' mess. Both his parents had died during World War II, and his uncles and aunts were only too pleased when he decided there was nothing for him to do in his hometown, and he would try his luck in the capital.

The newcomer to Rome looked for a distant cousin and eventually found him and his family living in a crowded shack under an arch of one of the ancient ruined aqueducts in the Mandrione district on the southeastern outskirts of the city. The cousin allowed him to stay there until Eduardo could arrange for some other shelter. Eduardo was then so slim that he took up little space sleeping on the floor of his cousin's shack, which had been put together with packing crates, chunks of concrete picked up at nearby building projects, tarpaper, corrugated iron, and other makeshift materials—a rickety monument to arrangement.

The cousin, his wife, and their two younger children still live in the same place. The shack now has a new roof and better flooring, a big refrigerator, a color TV, and a phone. But it is still dank and unsanitary.

Eduardo's cousin drives a truck that he bought second-hand, and vaguely says he is "trading in everything." He may be doing shady business with a tribe of gypsies who turn up from time to time in the scruffy neighborhood. Whatever the cousin is living on, he appears to be doing all right. He still speaks in southern dialect, although he has been a Roman of sorts for much longer than Eduardo, whose hometown accent has all but disappeared.

Eduardo spent most of his first weeks in the capital at the Termini railroad station, carrying travelers' suitcases for less money than the licensed porters asked. Inevitably he got in trouble with them. He also touted gypsy cabs, having arranged with their drivers for a small kickback from their inflated fares. Eventually he met a lieutenant of his former army outfit, a Roman who was on his way home. It developed that the lieutenant's brother was running an espresso bar and needed help handling takeout orders. The lieutenant remembered Eduardo's mess-hall service and gave him the espresso job.

A runner for a bar must be able to balance a tray loaded with full cups and glasses, spoons, paper bags filled with sugar, sandwiches, and pastry. He must look clean and must be quick so that the coffee is still hot on arrival. It helps if he is cheerful without being fresh. Eduardo seems to have been a success from the start.

The bar he was working for, not far from the railroad terminal, was—and still is—very busy. It has a reputation for coffee with a rich taste that lingers in your mouth. It also has a choice location near two government departments, the ministries of agriculture and of the treasury. Offices of lawyers and business firms are all around.

With his boyish smile and quick repartee, Eduardo soon became the pet of the woman employees to whom he brought morning *cappuccino.* Some would stroke his curly hair and tap his muscular arms, telling him to keep the change. He did small errands for office workers, like darting to the pharmacy across the street for a couple of aspirins or to the tobacconist for a pack of cigarettes. He boasts that a few of the secretaries took a more lively interest in him.

More important to Eduardo's career, he managed to become an agent for some lawyers and middlemen who had dealings with the government. These busy people with attaché cases would often stop at the bar where he worked to use the pay phone and make sure the bureaucrat they were supposed to meet was actually in the office. In Rome it is useless to make appointments far ahead of time.

In most espresso bars everybody can hear what is being said into the pay phones because there are no booths. Once

Eduardo overheard a lawyer voicing disappointment after he was told a section chief in the Agriculture Ministry wouldn't be in that morning. Eduardo happened to know the official, who was a client, and he saw the official's secretary every morning when he rushed her a *"cappuccino* without foam" and a big croissant. Eduardo told the frustrated lawyer he could take a message to her, and might even be told when the official would be available.

Similar favors helped make Eduardo into something of a little power broker. After a few months he was able to give bar patrons advice on how to go about getting a decision on a tax case—the Finance Ministry was then still in the same building as the Treasury—or on procedures for obtaining a government loan for farming development. An agricultural cooperative started paying him a small retainer for tip-offs on the date when an influential committee in the nearby ministry was going to hold a meeting, and similar inside information.

All this I learned from Eduardo bit by bit. When I first met him, he had long before given up his espresso job and was a well-established fixer with bureaucratic and business contacts all over the city. He had been recommended to me by friends who had heard me complain that I was unable to get a phone in a new apartment. Less than a week after I had paid Eduardo a reasonable consideration, the telephone workers came and connected the phone.

People now call Eduardo *ragioniere,* which means accountant, or even *dottore,* although he never got beyond elementary school. But by the time he started military service he must already have known a lot about "arranging" things. He told me once that on his first day in the army, he and other raw recruits were fretting because they hadn't been given enough bed sheets and blankets. "Stop bitching," a corporal bellowed. *"Arrangiatevi!"* (literally, "arrange yourself"). Eduardo sneaked up to the second floor of the barracks building and scrounged bedding from the bunk of a soldier whose unit was out on a march.

If "arranging" came from military slang, as it probably did, it has by now lost all barrack connotations. It is one of the basic and most frequent terms in the Roman idiom. The phrase says plenty about the technique of survival in a city that over the centuries has been afflicted by all sorts of calamities. Romans know by experience and instinct that human relations are ambiguous, fortune is fickle, unforeseen things happen all the time, and yet one has to get through the day, indeed through life, somehow.

Rome at the end of World War II offered the spectacle of an entire city getting by through "arrangement," and snapping back to a semblance of prosperity. British visitors in the late 1940s didn't believe their eyes when they saw elegantly dressed Romans eating golden fettuccine dripping with butter in their cheerful restaurants at a time when London, the capital of a victorious and still imperial power, was cold, dark, and hungry. The secret of what was then called the "Italian miracle" was, at least in the capital, an "arrangement"—a thriving black market that was able to provide everything from eggs to steaks, from American cigarettes to then rare penicillin.

Today, there is no black market to speak of, but the "arrangement" has remained. It is the way Romans manage to disentangle themselves from difficulties, mobilize family connections and friends, carry on complicated love affairs, avoid paying taxes, cope with strikes and the breakdown of public services, and grapple with any and all emergencies.

SYSTEMIZING

Silvana has been upset ever since the beginning of the year because her longtime friend, Bruno, spent Christmas and New Year's Eve with his family instead of with her. A year earlier, and all the ten or eleven years before, Bruno and Silvana had been together during the holidays, either in Rome or in some winter resort in the mountains, once even on safari in Kenya.

Now Silvana, who is in her thirties, suspects that Bruno wants to ditch her. They have many fights during which she keeps repeating, "You have got to systemize me!" She recently told him this in a late-evening phone call to his home that seemed to have embarrassed him, as it was meant to do. His wife must have been nearby while he kept saying into the phone in a bland voice, "Okay, okay, certainly, we'll talk about it," as if he were speaking to a business associate.

Sistemare, "to systemize." Silvana, in her verbal broadsides, is firing off a term that is almost as essential to the Roman vocabulary as are the various forms of "to arrange." *Sistemazione* means to be done at last with all the flimsy arrangements, no longer to lie awake worrying every night. It means stability, security, a marriage perhaps, an income one can count on, a steady job, ownership of one's apartment—and it always means prestige in a society where people often keep afloat by day-to-day "arrangements."

To be systemized is a dream that many Romans pursue. Silvana, who lives in a small place off the Corso Trieste, a middle-class neighborhood, where Bruno pays the rent, wants him to give her three or four apartments—one as a place to stay permanently, the others to provide income for her.

Systemizing Silvana in the way she demands shouldn't be impossible for Bruno, because he is in the construction business. He is no longer doing as well as he used to, but he and his cousins, who are the senior partners in a group of interlocking building companies, still deal with new apartment houses in different parts of the city. They control scores, maybe hundreds, of unsold and vacant housing units.

The family enterprise began when Bruno's cousins inherited a small contracting firm in a town in the Abruzzi. At the end of World War II they moved to Rome, where they bought up land on the city's outskirts. Most of it had been owned by people who needed money or were eager to ride the postwar building boom—religious orders and other church bodies, and princes, marquesses, and counts of the "black," or papal, aristocracy.

After a few successful ventures, Bruno's cousins had no trouble obtaining bank credit to buy, subdivide, and develop large chunks of real estate. They were leaders in the reckless band of entrepreneurs who in a couple of decades ringed the Italian capital with a broad belt of concrete.

The family-owned apartment houses, which usually looked decrepit after only a few years, marched out in all directions onto the *campagna Romana,* the plain encircling the city that was for centuries a realm of malaria and brigandage, but yet had charmed romantic visitors with its ancient ruins, loneliness, and grandiose vistas.

While the excavation equipment was chewing up more of the *campagna Romana,* Bruno was busy working on city departments, trying to secure the necessary building permits. In Rome's overall zoning plan, the area where Bruno's cousins had started a new project might have been designated for a public park with playgrounds. It was Bruno's task to persuade one of the municipal bureaucrats to propose a change in the master plan, which the appropriate commission would routinely approve. Bruno's job had always been to establish connections with influential people. He was good at it. Bruno's cousins installed a sales agent in a ground-floor office of one of their half-finished buildings, and prospective residents chose apartments and signed condominium contracts. In most cases, no one had bothered about streets, water supply, sewers, or other city services in the still rural zone.

The pioneer inhabitants of the new outlying neighborhood had a rough time the first few months. They had to muster all their skills at "arranging" things. Prodded by Bruno, however, the city eventually built an asphalt road to the inchoate suburb and gave it a name chosen by a special "toponymic committee." The project was linked with the municipal water and electric power networks, and a sanitation truck started appearing every now and then to pick up the garbage. Bruno also advised the new homeowners on how to stage sit-ins and demonstrations in the center of Rome to get telephones installed and how to goad the city's transit system into extending a bus line to the new community.

Another one of Bruno's chores was to stave off labor trouble. His cousins tried to hire bricklayers and other laborers —mostly immigrants from the deep south—who belonged to no union, but there were always some militants who tried to organize them and incite them to strikes. Bruno sometimes managed to make deals with the activists.

I've met Bruno only once and probably wouldn't recognize him if I saw him again. But I know plenty about him and his cousins through the constant gossip that makes it hard to keep any secrets, or even defend one's privacy, in this city. Bruno's clan is frequently mentioned in the newspapers. One of his cousins, the chief of the family enterprise, was for years the president of one of Rome's two first-league soccer clubs. A rich man must occupy such a post. The club's finances are always in a mess, the cost of its star players is enormous, and ticket sales bring in much less than they should because at every match thousands of fans get into the stadium without paying. The president must periodically help out with money of his own, which he never sees again.

Nevertheless, in the years when the building industry in Rome was roaring, a soccer team presidency was excellent for public relations and brought with it considerable prestige and influence. Traffic cops would tear up the ticket they were writing out as soon as they realized they had flagged down the famous sports executive. City officials would fawn on him in the hope of getting a free pass to championship events. Banks would not complain about making yet another business loan. Even his own construction workers would be more cooperative when his team beat the Milan club.

Two years ago, Bruno's cousin resigned from his sports post, explaining that he had to devote all his energies to securing continued employment for his workers. The construction boom had markedly slowed down, cash was no longer plentiful, and he felt that more soccer fame might only attract unwelcome attention from kidnappers. He had, of course, been protected by private bodyguards—whom he used to call "my gorillas"—day and night for years, but now he thought it safer to withdraw into relative obscurity and keep out of the newspaper sports sections and off television.

Bruno probably has much less money than his cousins do, but gangsters might not know this. He too is afraid of publicity, Silvana says. She has threatened to do something that will get his name into the press if he doesn't see to it that she becomes an apartment owner. Bruno isn't a movie star or a television personality, so the scandal magazines wouldn't be interested in him and his woman troubles. Still, he seems uneasy in the face of Silvana's campaign for a *sistemazione,* and the chances are she will have her way. To win what she wants, Silvana says she is ready to fight. Tears, rows, reconciliations, threats, scenes at Bruno's office or even in his home are weapons in Silvana's arsenal. Some have already been tested; others are in readiness.

Silvana was once Bruno's secretary, but he talked her into

giving up the job shortly after their romance began, and since then she has been living on his handouts. Silvana thinks Bruno didn't want her to continue working in his office because of jealousy: subcontractors, home buyers, and many other men come and go all day. Another reason may have been that Bruno didn't want her to know too much about his business dealings and his true relations with his wife, who had a habit of phoning the office several times a day.

Bruno seems to have been fairly generous with money and gifts during the first few years of his affair with Silvana. She settled into a languid existence—sleeping late in the morning, having lunch or dinner with the busy real estate executive at some chic restaurant, buying clothes, having her hair done, chatting with woman friends on the phone or going to the movies with them, and waiting for Bruno's next visit or phone call while she watched television.

Every now and then Bruno would take a few days off on various pretexts and they would take a trip to Venice or Switzerland. The safari in East Africa was financed in part by Bruno's cousins, who wanted him to look into the prospect of building supermarkets in Kenya. On his return, Bruno advised his cousins, wisely, to stick to Rome and leave overseas projects to contractors with more experience and greater resources.

In the first sultry year of their romance, Bruno kept telling Silvana he wanted to marry her, if Italy would only introduce divorce. Then, at the end of 1970, Parliament did just that, and in a referendum in 1974 the Italian electorate voted three to two to uphold the new divorce legislation. It was the hour of truth for Bruno, as it was for uncounted other Romans who for years had been carrying on triangular relationships, always making day-to-day arrangements, always sighing to their lovers, "If only I could get a divorce."

Maybe Bruno had thought at first that it would be nice to live with the pretty, young Silvana—even to be married to her. But when at last he could have talked about a divorce with his wife, Bruno was in no hurry. He told Silvana he wanted to wait until his children—a teenage daughter and a younger son—were through school, because just then they needed his stern presence. Silvana says the children hardly see their father and do what they like anyway.

She also suspects that Bruno never really wanted to end his marriage. It seems Bruno's wife is vaguely aware that he had once been going out with his secretary, but is half convinced that her husband's fling is over. Silvana, recalling past Christmases when she and Bruno were both at her place in Rome, now believes that he managed to spend some time with his family as well. Yuletide is hectic for many Romans, who stolidly eat two Christmas dinners—an early one and a late one—to keep their wives and their girl friends happy.

After Bruno's defection during the recent holidays, Silvana served him with an ultimatum: either he systemizes her by giving her three or four desirable apartments or she will tell everything to his wife.

There is a fall-back position in Silvana's ultimatum, however. She tells me she would be content with just one apartment if he moved in with her and started talking with his wife, through lawyers, about a divorce. But being, as she says, a realist, she doesn't think Bruno wants such a *sistemazione.*

SOCCER SCANDAL

Policemen searched the Olympic Stadium for bombs and weapons before they went on around-the-clock guard duty the Saturday afternoon before the big event. On Sunday morning, packs of militant fans began to arrive at the concrete oval between the Tiber River and the steep eastern slope of Monte Mario. The Romans call this event their derby, but it has nothing to do with horses. It is the passion-rousing biannual championship game between the leading local soccer teams—the Roma and its archrival, the Lazio.

The chronic tension between supporters of the two teams had increased throughout the city during the week. In offices, workshops, espresso bars, and taverns, Romanisti and Laziali taunted each other. Fan clubs met to rehearse their battle cries and paint grossly provocative signs for display at the stadium. Soccer enthusiasts rashly promised to pay for liters of wine, dress up in the colors of the adversary camp, or submit to various other indignities if their side lost.

However, at the stadium on Sunday the mood seemed less boisterous than usual. During the last derby, in October, a Lazio fan in the bleachers had been hit by a small rocket fired from across the field where the most turbulent Roma backers, called the "ultras," were clustered. The victim's wife, with admirable presence of mind, had at once pulled the missile out of his eye socket, where it was sticking, but he was dead on arrival at the hospital. At the stadium, the game went on as if nothing had happened.

This time the authorities were taking no chances. Policemen frisked spectators and seized anything that might serve for attack, especially sticks and metal bars attached to banners in the clubs' colors—yellow and purple for the Roma, blue and white for the Lazio. Bottles and metal cans were banned from the stadium; soft drinks were sold in plastic containers, coffee in paper cups.

Normally, the stadium would have been filled to overflowing for the Roma-Lazio match. The structure, built for the 1960 Olympic Games and now dilapidated, has a capacity of eighty thousand spectators, but barely fifty thousand showed up this time. There was plenty of space in the vast parking lots outside.

Uneasiness was palpable, and the heavy clouds hanging over Rome deepened the gloom. Players, sports officials, and fans all seemed uncomfortable, not because they remembered the absurd violence of the autumn derby and resented the new security measures, but because of recent disclosures about corruption in soccer. A few weeks after the game, four members of the Lazio team, together with stars of other clubs, were in jail on charges of "aggravated and continued fraud" by game fixing. The scandal shook the entire powerful soccer establishment to its foundations.

About forty prominent members of the Italian financial community happened to be in prison at the same time, in the wake of an entirely unconnected banking scandal, but their misfortune hardly impressed anyone. Instead, millions of Italians were far more deeply shocked by the soccer affair than they were when President Giovanni Leone was forced to resign owing to alleged improprieties. Romans are cynical about their financiers and politicians, but they believe in the haughty young athletes who, for kicking a ball across the lawn, are paid far better than an ambassador or an army general.

Soccer is to uncounted Romans what religion is in an age of faith. No wonder Bruno's cousin found the team presidency a business asset. Soccer gives meaning to otherwise drab lives, populates imaginations with a pantheon of demi-gods, provides a simple code of ethics in the fair-play rules of the ball game, enacts a continual drama of good against evil—Roma versus Lazio, or the other way around—and supplies an emotionally satisfying ritual on Sundays after litanies of speculation and comment during the week.

The crowd in the Olympic Stadium is usually much larger than that in St. Peter's Square, where many of those cheering the Pope are pilgrims from the provinces and tourists from abroad. By far the majority of spectators in the stadium are men, soccer being a macho thing. Fans go to the match with male friends or maybe with their sons, but they would rather leave their womenfolk at home. The presence of the rocket victim's wife at that derby was noted as an exception.

Thousands of local soccer widows know they cannot count on their husbands on Sundays because the men must discuss the forthcoming game in the neighborhood bar over their morning espresso, troop off to the stadium, and watch television replays with comments by experts late into the night. Giulia, a friend of mine who is married to a Laziale with an insurance job, says she doesn't mind that her husband drives to the stadium right after their early Sunday lunch. "If he didn't have the Lazio he might have a mistress," she remarks with equanimity.

Another acquaintance of mine, Pierluigi, feigns to be much more of a Roma fan than he actually is. He thus has Sunday afternoons off and is able to take a succession of girl friends to the movies when his wife believes he is cheering on his team.

Before the recent Roma-Lazio derby the authorities had seen to it that the most savage or scurrilous graffiti on the flaking stadium walls were chalked over. Still the smoldering hostility between the two camps led to incidents. The police broke up scuffles and detained a few particularly aggressive youths. Some two hundred Roma rooters started chanting: "Ten, a hundred, a thousand Paparellis!" Vincenzo Paparelli was the Laziale who died in the mini-missile attack during the October game. The presumed assailant, a young member of a Roma fan club who had been identified by the police, was still a fugitive, and everyone wondered who was shielding him. (He gave himself up months later, never revealing where he had been hiding.)

In the boiling stadium the supporters of the two "clans" —the Roma and the Lazio—were heirs to the rivalries, hatred, and intrigues that pitted the patricians (identified with Lazio fans) against the plebeians (Roma fans) in the social conflicts of the Roman Republic, and the Reds against the Greens in the chariot races of the circus in the imperial age. The idiom for soccer delirium is *tifo*, which means typhus fever; a fan is called a *tifoso*.

A man or boy isn't really a Roman unless he displays *tifo* for one of the two clubs. Immigrants from the provinces usually shift their loyalty from their hometown team quickly and become rabid Laziali or Romanisti and thus gain acceptance in the capital. It is all right, even popular, to show lack of interest and contempt for politics and politicians, but in the capital's lower middle class (the vast majority of the population) it would seem extremely odd not to root for either the Roma or the Lazio. Members of Parliament, big-name entertainers, prominent intellectuals—all attend soccer matches and discuss them with the media to prove they share the mass tastes and are part of the popular culture— genuine *tifosi*.

A Genoese industrialist and soccer fan with a scientific bent, Edmondo Costa, has found that *tifo* in Rome is more virulent than in the other big Italian cities. Using various criteria for quantifying soccer fever, he put Rome on top of the national scale with a 1.04 measurement, followed by Naples with 0.8, Turin with 0.6, and Milan with 0.5.

Rome's high pitch of soccer enthusiasm suggests that the capital fields the best teams in the nation and has something to be proud of in the world of spectator sports. Alas, this is not the case. Despite the huge amounts of money spent on players and coaches and the adulation surrounding them, the Roma and the Lazio give their backers little joy and much pain. The capital's two teams seldom reach the top of the national championship table and are often beaten by the clubs of the northern industrial centers, Milan and Turin, which are wealthier and better managed. Even the teams from poor Naples or smaller provincial towns often triumph over the Roman players.

A Roma or Lazio fan takes perverse pride in sticking to his team in adversity. Although he may boo its pampered players when they repair, crestfallen, to their locker rooms after a disgraceful defeat, next Sunday the inveterate *tifoso* will get up early, board a chartered bus to some faraway city, maybe Bologna or Bari, and give vocal support to his squad in an out-of-town game.

"One has to be a masochist to be a Romanista," said my friend Pietro after a particularly dismal team showing. I was visiting him at the San Giovanni Hospital. He was terminally ill, and it was the last time I saw him alive. He had been the driver in the Rome Bureau of the *New York Times,* and as long as I had known him the Roma had been his consuming interest. For many years it had been an office joke on Mondays to present Pietro with hypocritical condolences on the latest Roma debacle. He would just shake his head. He still shook his head about the terrible performance of his team, though he couldn't expect ever to see them play again.

The sociology of Roman soccer is largely unexplored. The Lazio is the poorer of the two clubs, but many of its supporters are wealthy middle-class people, even rich noblemen. Some Laziali belong to the lumpen proletariat of the suburbs, others are in business. The man who was killed by the rocket had been running an automobile repair shop. Right-wing people and neofascists are rarely Romanisti; the big black swastikas that were freshly painted on the stadium walls just before the derby were surely the handiwork of Laziali.

The setting of the Olympic Stadium, incidentally, inspires right-wing nostalgia. The soccer shrine rises in what was once known as the Mussolini Forum, now Italic Forum, a complex of sports installations built during the Fascist dictatorship. A gold-tipped marble obelisk near the stadium carries to this day the large inscription "DUX," leader, the Latin root for the Italian word *Duce* by which Mussolini wanted to be addressed. Fascist symbols abound in mosaics laid out around the area.

The Roma, on the other hand, is backed by many Christian Democrats, including government members, and by Communists. Throughout the city and its outskirts the Roma has many more fan clubs than the Lazio. While one of the Lazio bulwarks is the well-to-do Parioli district, where Mussolini's era seems to linger on, Romanisti prevail in the suburbs that vote red. There is also an extremist fringe. At the derby game a group of militant Romanisti youths showed up with their heads wrapped in Palestinian-style checkered cloths; they said they were "fedayeen."

This derby game had its casualty too. A fifty-four-year-old spectator on a cheap seat collapsed when the Roma scored the winning goal in the second half of the game, and died shortly afterward. Fans suffering heart attacks in the excitement of the match are routine. Nobody makes much of a fuss about such deaths in the stadium; the newspapers devote only a few lines to them.

The 110th derby was won by the Roma, two to one. Jubilant rooters in the stadium set off firecrackers. In some neighborhoods of the city later in the afternoon, groups of Romanisti paraded in mock funerals behind a bundle, looking like a coffin, wrapped in the Lazio's blue and white. Fans of the losing team grimly ordered the wine they had undertaken to pay for in case of a Roma victory.

The headquarters of the state-controlled soccer-pool agency announced that each of the six fortunate participants who correctly guessed the outcome of the Roman derby and of the twelve other first-league championship games had won nearly half a billion lire—$550,000 at the prevailing rate of exchange. The 370 bettors who got the results of twelve out of the thirteen matches received about $8,000 each.

In a nation where between 12 and 15 million people, including many women who have never seen a match, fill in the soccer-pool slips every week, close to a million legal bets are placed in the capital alone. Nobody knows how much money changes hands in clandestine betting, but it is estimated that for the Roman derby alone, close to a million dollars is illegally at stake. Why do gamblers bypass the official soccer pool? Primarily, to avoid taxes. The underground betting also has an advantage in that one can concentrate on just one game—such as the derby—rather than have to call the outcome of all the thirteen championship matches. The racketeers who control the betting syndicates have neatly carved up the city into zones of operation, and everything functions just fine.

Walter-Ugo, who lives in Tormarancio, an eastern suburb that looks ragged but has pockets of hidden wealth from shadowy sources, is among the clandestine gamblers. "I meet the fellow from the syndicate in the espresso bar near the cinema," he reports. "He has a mimeographed sheet with the chances of the impending games, and quickly puts me in touch with someone who will bet against me. There are no forms to fill, no questions asked, no computers. Sometimes the syndicate will even take bets by phone. If you win, you get the full amount at once. Losers pay up within the week. They know that if they don't, their car will be wrecked or maybe they will suffer a broken arm or leg."

The soccer scandal that was already brewing as the Lazio and the Roma faced each other in the stadium had its origins in the betting underground. It soon erupted in unprecedented force. A Roman restaurant operator and a wholesale fruit and vegetable dealer, through their lawyers, filed complaints with the state prosecutor's office charging that twenty-seven first-league soccer players took bribes from them to fix games, but failed to deliver. The allegations shook the soccer federation, one of Italy's biggest industries and a prime mover of money in the capital. It was like an earth tremor heralding the eruption of a volcano. Terrified sports figures scurried for safety.

Never mind that the move by the two complainants was self-incriminatory. Although they freely admitted that they had engaged in illegal betting, thus confessing to an offense, they risked little on that count—a fine or, at most, imprisonment of up to three months.

The alleged bribes slipped to soccer stars were a different matter, however, and posed a legal problem. Under the penal code, corruption is punishable only when public officials or persons entrusted with public services are implicated; nowhere does the law state that members of a soccer team must not take money in exchange for a limp performance that will cause their side to lose a match.

It may of course be argued that a deal to fix a game is fraud when it is pulled off to trick unsuspecting bettors out of money. But can one be prosecuted for an alleged crime in a situation that is in itself a violation of the law, namely, clandestine betting? The judiciary branch of government, after some deliberation, said yes.

An investigating judge ordered the arrest of the duo that had claimed to have been double-crossed after "buying" games from corrupt soccer players. During questioning of the two complainants and of members of the soccer establishment who had been subpoenaed, remarkable things came to light.

Inquiries into Roman scandals are always like the exploration of newly discovered catacombs—the subterranean passageways point in all directions, unexpected twists reveal fantastic caves, heaps of stones and earth block further progress, the archaeologist may get lost in the underground labyrinth.

It seems the restaurateur and the fruit-and-vegetables dealer had been losing huge sums, mostly borrowed money, in bets on soccer games that they thought they had fixed.

They were pressed by their creditors and were threatened by the syndicate to pay up speedily, or else. Acquaintances of mine who patronized the seafood restaurant where one of the two self-confessed bribe payers acted as manager told me he had been carrying a gun under his jacket while glumly walking from table to table to greet guests.

He and his partner in the game-fixing plot reportedly called on officials of the clubs whose players they believed they had bought, and on the players themselves, frantically asking to be bailed out. Some clubs apparently coughed up the money, others didn't.

The soccer executives who helped out the two corrupters must have thought they had struck a reasonable bargain. Star players represent an investment that can run into millions of dollars in transfer fees, salaries, and bonuses. If they are disqualified by the soccer federation in the wake of a scandal, the club may face financial ruin. Paying hush money may be the minor evil.

When the restaurateur and the fruit-and-vegetables wholesaler eventually turned to the judiciary, the general understanding was that they only denounced players of clubs that hadn't paid up. In the ensuing flurry of rumors, there was also talk of at least one referee who was supposed to have taken bribes.

Among the witnesses questioned by the magistrates was a Franciscan friar, the Reverend Antonio Lisandrini, who for years had been serving as the "spiritual adviser" and a kind of mascot to the Lazio team. The sixty-two-year-old priest was a friend of actors and actresses and liked having his picture taken with them. He often traveled with the Lazio players and said mass for them in the lobby of their hotel on the mornings of out-of-town games. The Franciscan affected the earthy language of the locker room when he wasn't officiating at the altar. Rome's church authorities had let him play his self-chosen role, but the magistrates seemed to think he knew something about the briberies.

Three weeks after the Roma-Lazio derby the investigating

judge thought he had enough evidence for new arrest warrants. In the stadiums of Rome and five other cities, eleven players and the president of the Milan soccer club were detained a few moments after the referees signaled the end of the championship games. The athletes were allowed to shower, and most of them were spared the shame of handcuffs. The commercial value of the eleven soccer stars who were locked up was estimated to total $10 million.

The warrants had been signed on Saturday, but the Finance Guard, which had been entrusted with carrying them out, put off the arrests until after the championship round on Sunday afternoon. The delay was meant to avoid disturbances by fans and to salvage the day's soccer pool operations. What the Treasury skims off the pool money is, after all, a part of the national revenue.

Among the eleven players sent to jail were four members of the Lazio team. Officers of the Finance Guard came to get them in their locker room in the city of Pescara on the Adriatic coast right after the end of the game, which the Roman club lost, two to nothing, to the local eleven. The Pescara fans jeered at the four soccer stars from the capital as they were being driven off to the local prison, to be transferred to Rome in the evening.

The president of the Lazio, Umberto Lenzini, was close to tears and moaned, "What a disgrace!" Later, the Lazio president, a contractor, told reporters that he was unaware of any game fixing: "I have been betrayed."

Although the press and the state broadcasting system had for some time referred to *calcio truffa*, or fraudulent soccer, the show—the national championship and the soccer pool—must go on. On the Sunday after the crackdown, the Lazio was arrayed in the Olympic Stadium with four young players from the reserves replacing the stars who were in prison. To the delight of club officials, forty thousand Lazio diehards were in the bleachers. One fan club displayed a large sign reading "Persons Come and Go, the Lazio Remains." The fans were like votaries of a fanatic sect proclaiming their intention to keep the faith even though their prophets and priesthood have just been exposed as impostors and frauds.

The rejuvenated team, quickly dubbed the "Baby Lazio," played the visiting Catanzaro from the deep south, and in a lusty performance trounced it, four to nothing. It was the first Lazio victory in months. The four Lazio stars who were being held in the decrepit Queen of Heaven Jail near the Vatican must have had ambivalent feelings on learning that their team had been victorious without them.

The four were soon free on bail, as were the other imprisoned players. The restaurateur and the fruit-and-vegetables dealer were granted "provisional liberty" without bail in recognition of their collaborating with justice.

It was safe to predict the sequel. In all Roman scandals, lawyers raise legal exceptions, adopt dilatory tactics, file defamation suits, quibble endlessly when a trial does in fact take place, and appeal to higher courts if their clients are found guilty. In the meantime, the police and the magistrates lose interest in older cases that no longer make headlines. Witnesses fall ill, disappear, or say they can't remember anything. The head of state may ultimately proclaim an amnesty to reduce the backlog of pending court cases and provide some breathing space in the overcrowded prisons.

The game-fixing affair was no exception. When the trial opened several months later, the judicial authorities had decided to hold it in a hall near the Olympic Stadium big enough to accommodate the large courtroom audience they expected—but very few people turned up, most of them relatives of the accused soccer stars. Rome had almost forgotten the scandal, and a new championship season was underway.

The trial fizzled out with the acquittal of all thirty-three soccer players and the three club presidents who were in the dock, although many of them had confessed to throwing games. There is no article on the statute books that prohibits participants in a sports contest from taking bribes, the three-judge court ruled. Where there is no law, there is no crime, according to the ancient wisdom of Roman law. The only defendant to be punished was the fruit dealer. The court fined him the equivalent of $350 for a technical offense— postdating the checks he gave to corrupt players.

But there was to be a final reckoning of another sort. The Finance Guard began to audit hundreds of reputed big earners in the soccer industry to make sure they paid income tax on every lira they had made, legally or otherwise, during the last several years. The appeals against the assessments will keep tax lawyers busy for years.

TAXING SIROCCO

The crowd pressing against a closed green door and wooden police barriers outside the district office of the internal revenue service near St. Peter's Square was rebellious. "They don't give a damn about us citizens, they are treating us like dung," said a middle-aged man—perhaps a store owner or a real estate salesman. "And then they are surprised when somebody takes a gun and starts shooting at them." The protester didn't need to specify who "they" are. Everybody around him understood that he meant not only the fiscal bureaucrats upstairs who worked with exasperating slowness, but also their superiors, the finance minister, all ministers, the government, Parliament, all politicians, the entire system.

The mutinous outburst set off a wave of nodding and muttering: "He's right," and "What a scandal, they are disgusting." A woman who looked as if she had left all her jewelry at home to appear less affluent at her meeting with the tax auditor was close to tears. "I got this summons only yesterday," she explained to the flustered policeman who was supposed to control the crowd. "Now look at this date stamp; it was sent more than a week ago. Is it my fault that the mail took so long? It says here I'll have to pay a 27 percent fine if I don't clear up my tax situation by today. I was here at eight, long before the office opened, and there were already fifty people. Now it's eleven, the office will close in an hour, and there is no movement at all. I certainly won't make it upstairs in time. What am I to do?" The policeman said uncomfortably that his job was only to keep order, he wasn't responsible for the tax office, one must have patience, *pazienza*.

The trouble is, nobody had patience on this particular day. Rome was oppressed by a sirocco that gripped the city like a giant migraine. As a matter of fact, I'd known the previous morning that the sirocco was on, even before I opened the bedroom blinds, because I had awakened with a dull headache. Many Romans and longtime residents do the same on such days. Newcomers may just experience a vague uneasiness, or may not feel anything wrong at all, and will wonder why other people seem edgy. The effects of the sirocco are cumulative, like radiation, or the lassitude that expatriates from temperate zones develop in the Tropics.

An early sirocco warning had come three days earlier, when a Tunisian who said he had a hand grenade hijacked an Italian airliner shortly after takeoff from Rome and ordered the captain to fly to Tripoli. The Libyan authorities radioed that Tripoli airport was closed owing to heavy sandstorms, so the commandeered plane landed in Palermo, where the hijacker surrendered after many hours of negotiations and on being promised he wouldn't be extradited to Tunisia. The hand grenade turned out to be a fake.

By that time, the hot, dry wind from the Sahara was already gusting across the Mediterranean at up to 60 miles an hour, picking up moisture.

When I stepped out into the street, still migrainous, I met the art expert who lives two floors below me. He was disgustedly gazing at his car, which was parked in the little square in front of our doorway and looked as if it had a peculiar form of measles or had been driven under a shower and sprinkled with loam. The car, which is blue, was covered with reddish-brown spots, and the other autos in the square were also polka-dotted with Sahara sand that the sirocco had deposited. "I had the car washed yesterday," the art expert said morosely. "Whenever I do, you may be sure we'll have sirocco."

It wasn't raining in the morning, but there must have been a drizzle, heavy with sand, during the night. The sky was leaden. I wondered whether something was wrong with my eyes, because the building facades up and down the street seemed to dance and I had difficulty focusing. Ah yes, of course, all those particles from Africa in the air.

At the corner bar, Carlo, the counterman, who is usually genial and garrulous, didn't even say hello. He just slapped a *cappuccino* in front of me. It tasted funny. The other people in the espresso bar seemed listless; nobody said much. Worse things happen during sirocco. Some Romans become suicidal, many others act depressed or violent when the unnerving south wind blows.

Foreigners who intend to spend some time in Rome and say they are puzzled by all the fuss about the reputedly sinister wind may be told at a cocktail party, "If you plan to kill somebody, do it when the sirocco is on—you'll be granted extenuating circumstances, maybe even go free." This isn't strictly true. Before a recent reform, Italian criminal law did cut the penalty for murder to as little as three years in prison if the victim was a spouse caught in adultery or one's daughter or sister whose "illegitimate carnal relation" with someone had just been discovered. However, these legal discounts on punishment for a "crime of honor" didn't say anything about sirocco. A clever lawyer might nevertheless still make a case under article 89 of the penal code, pleading "partial mental failure" brought on by the evil wind from Africa.

As the sirocco pushed heavy gray clouds northward, so deep as almost to touch the dome of St. Peter's, the mood outside the tax office on the Via della Conciliazione grew seditious. When an employee upstairs incautiously opened a window to look down at the unruly crowd, he was greeted with a barrage of insults, especially that Roman all-purpose invective, *stronzo* (turd).

Taxpayers who were dejectedly trickling out of another door of the building reported that the office staff upstairs was disagreeable. A white-faced man with a large envelope under his arm said: "They wouldn't listen to me, sent me from one room to the other, and eventually told me I'll have to pay for twice the amount I have earned. Where is a bar around here? I need a double brandy."

Earlier in the month, the office on the Via della Conciliazione had sent out notices to 121,000 residents of the city stating that their income tax returns, filed three years earlier, had been found to be inaccurate, incomplete, or mistaken. Unless the discrepancies were cleared up within twelve days, the tax liabilities would be increased and stiff fines would have to be paid, the notifications warned.

Most of the unwelcome letters from the district office were delivered late, and many might still be lying around post offices. Tens of thousands of Romans had flocked to the Via della Conciliazione during the last few days, but only a few hundred had the stamina or luck to see one of the handful of officials upstairs. The premises were cramped because files and unprocessed tax returns were stacked in all the rooms and corridors.

Years ago the Finance Ministry bought a large American computer system, but it still lacked the programmers and other personnel to make it work properly. The entire scene at the district office looked like another instance of the bureaucratic ineptitude that seems to be the norm in Rome.

The office on the Via della Conciliazione was receiving taxpayers three times a week from eight-thirty A.M. to noon. Each interview took at least twenty minutes. At the sluggish pace of a sirocco day, it might require ten years to review all the 121,000 tax cases. And what about the returns that were filed last year and the year before?

In the afternoon, the sirocco that had been weighing on Rome for thirty-six hours dissolved in rain. After dark, the wind turned eastward and the showers stopped. One felt relief, as if a nightmare had lifted or a hangover had finally abated.

Early next morning I was awakened by the loud chirping

88

of the sparrows, linnets, and other birds that indomitably nest among the roofs, terraces, campaniles, and cupolas of central Rome. Sunlight glinted through the blinds. The sky was cloudless and brilliant, the ochre and the other colors of the cityscape were vivid. It was cold, and the air was uncommonly clear; from my vantage point in the heart of Rome I could distinctly see every single pine tree on top of Monte Mario three miles away. The *tramontana*—the exhilarating wind from the north, from the Alpine glaciers and the snowcapped Apennine peaks—had changed the collective temper of Rome overnight. The sanitation man who vigorously swept the street without sidewalks on which I live actually smiled at me. The delivery boy of the corner grocery was singing a pop number as he flitted by on his bicycle. Carlo, the *barista,* drew me into a loud exchange of views with two other patrons, and we all agreed that most soccer championship games are fixed.

At the district office across the Tiber River, it was the day when the public is barred and the staff is supposed to tackle the backlog of unprocessed tax returns. The officials were relaxing over *cappuccinos.* Downstairs there was only the policeman who yesterday had been hard put to calm the irate crowd of frustrated taxpayers, and today might be watching out for terrorists. "Let's hope the *tramontana* is still blowing tomorrow when the public is admitted again," he said. "Everybody is more good-natured when the weather is right. We depend so much on winds."

SUBWAY CARNIVAL

Some weeks before the soccer derby in Rome, the city's first really useful subway line started running. Rome's carnival, the Mardi Gras celebration, was about to end just as the rapid transit system opened. High school students deserted their classes to ride boisterously back and forth on the new line all morning. On the first Sunday of the subway operation, entire families tried the novelty, enjoying picnic lunches in the new underpass that links the Spanish Square with the Via Veneto, and clogging the subway so that other would-be passengers had to be barred for hours.

On Mardi Gras itself, the new Metropolitana was filled with children dressed up as Snow Whites and spacemen, Pierrots, gypsies, and cowboys. Stations and coaches were littered with confetti and paper streamers. Roman carnival had long ago come to this—little boys and girls parading in the streets, and more recently in the subway, showing off their fancy dresses, their faces heavily made up (producing sadly equivocal expressions), some wearing small masks. An old police ban on public mummery by adults is still being generally observed. In a time of terrorism and spreading crime, the authorities can hardly be expected to lift the veto and expressly allow teenagers and adults to roam the streets masked, if only for a day.

There are many Mardi Gras parties in private homes, but the celebrations are a far cry from the Roman carnival of the nineteenth century, when carriages drove up and down the Corso, the city's most beautiful women hurled handfuls of confetti at onlookers, and visitors from all over Europe joined in the merrymaking that went on all over the city until the Ave Maria bell rang to signal the beginning of Lent as lines of papal soldiers cleared the streets and dance halls. "So gay, so bright and lively," reported Charles Dickens, who witnessed the end of carnival in Rome in 1846. "I shall always remember it."

The inauguration of the subway added a memorable feature to the carnival, which was otherwise like any other. Mercifully, there was no ribbon-cutting or speechmaking to mark the occasion, though a week before the underground system started regular service, the national government's transport minister said it was the largest public works project in the capital since the end of World War II. "No," the mayor rebutted, "it's the biggest project since the Colosseum was built."

The mayor's boast couldn't have been meant seriously. It may be debated, for instance, whether St. Peter's Basilica qualifies as a public works project, even though Christians all over Europe contributed money to it, but it surely beats the Metropolitana by its dimensions, let alone its architecture. The mayor also ignored the monumental baths of Emperors Caracalla and Diocletian and the walls around the city that Emperor Aurelian had built to protect it from barbarian invaders.

Impressive ruins of the imperial thermae and of the Aurelian walls have survived to this day. Even the huge stone ramparts that were built after last century's unification of Italy to harness the Tiber River compare with the new subway in sheer volume of work. So did the wholesale demolition of many city blocks that Mussolini ordered to create the large avenues leading to the Colosseum and St. Peter's—the Via dell' Impero and the Via della Conciliazione. The dictator's sycophants then glorified the "Third Rome," or Mussolinian Rome, as an era of architectural and civic splendor equal to the city of Emperor Augustus and that of the Renaissance popes. Nobody has yet spoken of a "fourth" Rome.

As for the Colosseum, it took the slaves of the Flavian emperors only eight years, A.D. 72–80, to erect the huge amphitheater. Two decades were needed for the new Metropolitana to proceed from blueprints to completion. During that time Rome saw seven mayors and nineteen national governments.

Taxpayers throughout Italy had to help finance the project because Rome, crushed by debts, was unable to shoulder the expenditure without assistance from the central government. By final reckoning, the subway cost $625 million.

Compared with the subway networks of New York, London, Paris, and Moscow, the new Metropolitana line, barely nine miles long, is a dwarf. Yet, for the Eternal City it was a giant breakthrough. Many Romans were convinced that their city would never have a real subway because every time anyone scratched the surface, archaeological finds came to light—the remains of an ancient temple, mausoleum, aqueduct, or monument, fragments of statuary, patches of mosaic, frescoed Christian catacombs, or other artifacts from Rome's 2,500-year history. The archaeologists of the government's fine arts and antiquities department would swoop down on the site like Roman motorists on a parking space, and the building project would be delayed indefinitely.

Over the years there have been many stories of private contractors finding ways to get around the archaeological hazards. Rumor surrounding some building projects had it that the site was covered with a big tarpaulin, and whatever emerged disappeared overnight: small objects were spirited away and big ones were bulldozed back into the ground. The construction workers didn't care. Thus, trouble with the antiquities experts was avoided and the project could go on. A statue, tablet, or mosaic that had been found might later be sold clandestinely and eventually would grace somebody's living room or garden.

The scholar-bureaucrats were vigilant during the subway work, but the archaeological yields weren't exceptional. For most of the route, the contractors tunneled far below the level of the ancient city. Among the few noteworthy finds during the subway project were a man-size statue of Jupiter, a sculpture of Bacchus, a monumental sarcophagus, the foundations of an aqueduct, and many remains of buildings that filled in blank spots on the scholars' maps of ancient Rome.

No historical discovery delayed work for long. The twenty years that elapsed before the bright lobster-colored trains of the new subway started running were lost to red tape, wrangling between two contracting companies, lack of coordination between the many departments of the city and national governments that claimed a say in the matter, financial difficulties, and strikes.

The archaeologists may have been far more thrilled when Rome built its very first subway in the early 1950s. At that time, workers unearthed the remains of an ancient lupanar, or bordello, when they were digging near the Colosseum. Such a find wasn't surprising, because the area was once an ill-famed neighborhood, known as the *suburra*, where gladiators, prostitutes, and adventurers from the provinces of the empire hung out. What did puzzle the scholars, according to stories that may or may not be apocryphal, was the discovery of early Christian symbols and inscriptions scratched into the walls of cell-like rooms. One possible explanation was that some of the girls who entertained visitors in the cubicles were Christians. Whatever the truth of the matter, it is rumored that the antiquities department, after consultation with the Vatican, advised the contractor to refill the ancient lupanar with earth and to change the subway route slightly so as to bypass the site. If the Christian graffiti in the bordello of the *suburra* ever existed, they have disappeared again.

The older subway line, which passes near the Colosseum, runs from the central railroad terminal southward to a point past the Circus Maximus, then emerges and proceeds on the surface to the World Fair district. This satellite town was to be the quintessence of the Third Rome. Its core is a cluster of huge, glaringly bright buildings in a style that was later to be called Mussolini-modern. Prominent among them is a cubistic version of the Colosseum that was meant to be a Palace of Italian Civilization. The monumental structures had been designed to house an international exhibition in 1942, marking the twentieth anniversary of the march on Rome by Mussolini's Blackshirts. World War II spoiled the grandiose plans; the World Fair was never held.

Il Duce had dreamed that millions of visitors from all parts of Italy and from abroad would come to the capital by train, and would use the subway to proceed straight to the Fascist jubilee show. But when the line was at last opened in 1955, Mussolini had been dead for close to ten years, and Romans joked that their first subway was going from nowhere to nowhere. The area of the abortive World Fair then seemed remote and eerie in its loneliness.

Since then, government departments have moved into the modernistic suburb, many other offices have joined them, and a residential belt has been added. Today the World Fair district is a vital, airy part of the expanding city, although its flavor may seem more that of Brasilia than of Rome. However, its subway link to the railroad terminal isn't popular. Thugs have terrorized passengers and slashed the plastic seats with knives. Trains are often stoned on the surface section, and no day passes without anonymous bomb threats. Everyone tries to avoid riding the World Fair line, although many commuters have no other choice for getting quickly to work and back home again.

The authorities have promised they will see to it that the just-opened subway line will be better protected. The route, with twenty-two stations, runs from a point on the southeastern outskirts with the rustic name Curate's Inn to the railroad terminal, traverses the center, crosses the Tiber River on a new concrete bridge—the twenty-fourth Tiber bridge within the city limits—and ends in the Via Ottaviano, a ten-minute walk from St. Peter's Square.

On the opening day, one of the things that struck Romans most was the pristine state of the underground walls: no graffiti in the subway stations and passages. But not for long. Soon obscene words and pictographs abounded: the Roma and Lazio soccer teams were praised and damned; the swastika and the distorted five-pointed star of the Red Brigades loomed malignantly. When in Rome, the spray-can artists do just as those in other cities do. Everywhere Rome's walls are eloquent. And who has a better right to decorate them? After all, the Italians invented the word *graffiti*.

TWO VICTIMS

The Red Brigade's star and the swastika, are, of course, only symbols, unlovely but harmless abstractions on the Metro's walls. But guns and bombs are all too real. Here is a picture of another kind.

Two youths on a motorscooter in the Mazzini district stop in front of a residential building that houses the Lebanese embassy. One of the two pulls a gun out of a bulging yellow envelope and starts firing at the policeman on duty. Hit two or three times, the uniformed guard totters into the doorway, apparently seeking cover. The attacker follows him, coolly finishes him off with two more shots, slips the dead man's submachine gun from his shoulder and his revolver from its holster, walks out unhurriedly, and rejoins his accomplice, who has been waiting on the scooter. The pair drive off and vanish in the traffic.

The murdered policeman was nineteen years old. Had he been permitted to finish his guard shift, he would have rushed to the railroad terminal three hours later to catch a train to his native village in Apulia in the deep south. The young Public Security guard was about to start a two-week furlough and had told other policemen how impatient he was to be with his family. His father is a poor plasterer; his mother works in the tobacco fields.

The usual acknowledgment by the terrorists came later than is customary, after the one P.M. broadcast had given the victim's name. The assassin had been firing at the uniform;

he obviously didn't know whom he had slain. Then a male voice called a local newspaper on behalf of the Front Line, one of several ultraleft groups in the terrorist underground, and announced matter-of-factly, "We have killed Maurizio Arnesano."

An hour later, another man called a news agency asserting that the murder had been carried out by the Armed Revolutionary Nuclei. This is a clandestine neofascist network, but the police tended to take the Front Line claim more seriously. Whoever did it, Maurizio was the sixth policeman killed by terrorists during the first six weeks of 1980. In the same period, four civilians were murdered in ideologically motivated violence.

During all of 1979, twenty-two persons, ten of them members of the police forces, died in attacks by political extremists. In 1980 the pace of terrorism was quickening: ten murders in six weeks averages one every four days. Many Romans turn off their sets whenever they are shown yet another corpse on a sidewalk, or when the president of the republic once again stands with bowed head as the victim lies in state. This time, the aged president was visibly shaken by the wild keening of the young policeman's mother, who, together with her husband, had been brought to the capital from Apulia.

Maurizio's father looked tearfully at the head of state and said in a voice thick with grief and anger: "All your politics stinks. When you catch the assassins, you let them go. Mr. President, is this just?" The head of state was silent for a few seconds, and then muttered, "No, I don't think this is just." The problem was that no terrorist had ever been caught red-handed.

Other people in Rome too asked questions. Why arm a nineteen-year-old with weapons he really hasn't learned to use? Why put him in uniform on the street as a conspicuous target? The investigators decided that the murder had nothing to do with Lebanon or the Middle East. Probably the terrorists just wanted to kill a policeman, any policeman. Why don't experienced plainclothesmen guard diplomatic missions?

At the nearby police station, a frightened colleague of the teenage victim, himself not much older, said: "We have been trained to shoot at cardboard targets twenty feet away and have had some karate lessons. But what can you do when you have a couple of slugs in your belly before you know who is attacking you?" A middle-aged woman in the building where the Lebanese embassy is housed said she'd known the murdered policeman by sight. "He smiled whenever I walked by," she recalled. *"Poveraccio,* he was just a boy."

Maurizio, like many other southerners, had volunteered for police duty instead of doing military service. The alternative offered by the induction rules is a way of finding enough recruits for the security forces. A young man who signs up for the police knows he will in due course receive regular pay and may stay with the force until retirement, unless he gets killed by terrorists or common criminals. Like many other southerners of military age, Maurizio had decided that a policeman's job was better then the prospect of finding no job at all on discharge from the armed forces. After a few months' training, the rookie policeman had joined the many men in uniform who stand or walk around Rome on guard duty.

People who must rely on such protection wonder how effective it really is. A senior American diplomat told me the other day that he was in his hotel one evening recently when he heard an explosion in the direction of the United States embassy on the Via Veneto. He walked over to the Palazzo Margherita, the ornate embassy building, and found it unharmed but without the customary detail of Italian police guards.

What had happened was that a bomb had gone off outside the offices of a foreign airline on the nearby Via Bissolati. The policemen on duty at the American embassy left their posts and ran over to the scene of the blast, apparently in the praiseworthy assumption that they might be needed. A couple of visitors from the Italian provinces who were on their way to the movies had been seriously wounded, and a clandestine Armenian group later assumed responsibility for the bombing. The diplomat remarked, "If the Red Brigades want to attack the American embassy they have only to set off a bomb a few blocks away, and then they can walk in without any trouble."

The bulk of the Italian security forces is made up of southerners. It's never mentioned in print in Italy, but people here often say that there is a culture gap between policemen from poor rural areas in Apulia, Calabria, and Sicily and the terrorists of the ultraleftist underground, who almost always have an urban background and often a college education. The murderous intellectuals quite often manage to outwit the less sophisticated lawmen, and seem to relish the game.

In the doorway where Maurizio was slain, neighborhood residents and shopkeepers laid flowers. But some weeks later the doorway was sprinkled with confetti, strewn by children celebrating carnival. At the espresso bar across the street, youngsters were cracking jokes and discussing the comparative merits of Italian and Japanese motorcycles.

Four days later, the Red Brigades struck at the top of the Roman establishment, assassinating the vice-president of the Superior Council of the Magistracy, Vittorio Bachelet. The slain jurist had been the deputy of the president of the republic in his role as head of the body that oversees the judiciary branch of government.

Professor Bachelet had just finished a lecture on administrative law at Rome State University in a hall named after his friend Aldo Moro, the murdered former prime minister. He was walking to another hall where faculty members and students were discussing the current wave of terrorism. A young woman tapped the fifty-three-year-old professor on the shoulder. He turned around, and she fired at him at point-blank range, joined by a young man who had come up from behind. He died instantly.

In the ensuing commotion, shouts of "The bomb! The bomb!" were heard. Panic. The murderers vanished, and the police said later that accomplices had raised the bomb alarm to facilitate their escape. There was no blast.

Police arrived in force and surrounded the university campus about an hour after the assassination. They checked the identity of teachers and students and searched a few before letting them go. At all campus gates there were droves of people clamoring to get out. An investigating magistrate arrived at the scene and ordered the police just to take away identity documents of all persons who left the campus. Professors and students, three thousand in all, were told they could pick up their documents at one of various police stations the next day. It isn't clear what the baffling procedure was supposed to achieve. Next day, faculty members and students lined up at police and Carabinieri headquarters for hours to get their identification documents back.

Of course, the assassins hadn't lingered on campus but had disappeared immediately after their crime. A getaway car was later found abandoned not far from the university complex. It was one of eight autos that presumed terrorists had stolen from two garages months ago, obviously to have a fleet of vehicles at their disposal. In the customary phone calls to newspapers, the Red Brigades declared they had "executed" Professor Bachelet.

Investigators theorized that the terrorist commando that carried out the murder was made up of at least eight persons, probably including some who had participated in the abduction and assassination of Mr. Moro. Some of the plotters must have been shadowing and fingering Professor Bachelet, others were probably positioned to spread panic, and two or three must have been waiting in as many cars just outside the campus.

Commentators on state television said that the loss of life through terrorist crimes had "morally" the same weight whether the victim was a nineteen-year-old policeman or a professor who substituted for the head of state in the self-governing council of the judiciary. Politically, however, the television editorialists added, the murder on the university campus was immensely more serious because it had to be interpreted as a brazen challenge to the head of state and the country's institutions. The president of the republic had recently denounced terrorism in passionate terms.

In a macabre ritual that was becoming all too familiar, the head of state and other high officials arrived at the university to look at a white sheet in a corner of a staircase in the political science department under which Professor Bachelet's body lay. Terrorism's victim No. 11 in six weeks.

Next day at his weekly general audience in the Vatican the Pope praised Professor Bachelet, who for several years had been president of Catholic Action in Italy, the organized laity within the church. At the funeral service in the church of St. Robert Bellarmine in the upper-class Parioli district two days after the assassination, the slain jurist's two brothers, both Jesuit priests, concelebrated mass with the cardinal vicar of Rome. Professor Bachelet's son, a twenty-four-year-old physicist who had rushed back from the United States, made a public prayer during the church rite.

"Let us pray also for those who have struck down my dear dad," Giovanni Bachelet said. "Let there be always words of pardon on our lips, and never words of revenge." After a few seconds of deep silence, the congregation spontaneously burst into applause—a surprising response during a requiem service.

A SAFE HOUSE

The mothers who bring their tots to the municipal day-care center in the Appio district every weekday morning say Simona is great because her charges take to her at once. A slim woman in her late twenties with a plain face and rebellious dark hair, she has an affectionate no-nonsense way with small children, gets them to play with little noise and almost no tears, even manages to have them lie down for their nap after lunch, and kisses each when the mothers—rarely a father—come to fetch them in the afternoon.

In the rundown building near the Piazza Vittorio where Simona lives on her own in a small apartment, she is considered shy and probably not too happy. She says hello to her neighbors when she meets them in the hallway but avoids speaking to them, except maybe when somebody's plumbing leaks and wet patches show on her ceiling or bedroom wall. The other people in the apartment house know that Simona has a kindergarten job and is divorced, and they must think she is casting about for a new relationship, apparently with little luck. Every now and then friends—not always the same —are seen visiting Simona; some man or woman stays overnight, then disappears. There is no super in the building, the front door is closed all the time, and it is hard to tell who is coming and going.

Simona tells colleagues that the apartment near the Piazza Vittorio, a tacky, bustling neighborhood between the central railroad terminal and the Lateran, is ideal for her, especially since the new subway line has started running. From the subway station deep below the outdoor market in the square, she reaches her day-care center in a few minutes. The apartment's location in one of the most congested areas of Rome might be called outright strategic in another respect—Simona runs a safe house for terrorists.

She has never said so expressly, but over a long period she has dropped enough hints to make it easy for me to draw my own conclusions about the way she functions on at least two levels: a legal existence as a licensed "social assistant" in the city services, and a clandestine existence linked to revolutionary violence. There may also be a strand of emotional attachment to figures in the underground "armed party," but she has hardly ever alluded to such an aspect of her life. In my many years in Rome I have of course known several people who in one way or another were mixed up in extremist groups of the left or right. But Simona is the person closest to the terrorist scene I was able to reach in two years of efforts to learn about it firsthand.

One of the reasons for the success of the Red Brigades, the Front Line, and kindred terrorist organizations in remaining elusive for so long is their distrust of anyone they haven't known for years and gradually initiated into conspiratorial action. In a talkative, easygoing city where nobody seems able to keep a secret, the leftist plotters have managed to protect themselves to a large extent from police infiltrators, agents provocateurs, and journalists. At least one suspected traitor was murdered.

I pieced together Simona's secret history. She first got in touch with terrorists when she was a psychology student at Rome State University. It started when she drifted into a "collective," an unstructured, semipermanent assembly of leftist students and young instructors, and took part in several demonstrations on campus and off. During an anti-American parade in downtown Rome that led to a riot in and around the Largo Argentina, a fellow student gave her a Molotov cocktail, and she threw it at a police squad car. Her companion also tossed a gasoline bomb and was at once arrested and hauled to Public Security headquarters. Simona got away. The fact that she had never been detained made her particularly valuable to the underground because the police didn't know of her, had no fingerprints or photo.

At the time of the riot, Simona was still living with her mother, who has long been separated from her father. The mother comes from a well-off Roman family and has inherited a part-time interest in a movie theater in addition to several apartments in various parts of the city. Simona's father, a small-time lawyer from the south, went to live with a mistress many years ago and is said to be something of an adventurer and probably a gambler. Simona never saw much of him as a child and hasn't been in touch with him for the last few years.

Her churchgoing mother saw to it that Simona had a traditional upbringing. The girl went through a mystical period when she had what must have been a crush on a nun at the private school on the Via Cola di Rienzo in the Prati district, an eminently middle-class neighborhood on the right bank of the Tiber, where her mother still lives. Simona attended the last years of high school at a state institution in Prati, the Terenzio Mamiani, which was then in the throes of continual student protests. She became interested in the left-wing student movement, a loosely organized but very vocal group that dominated her school and other units of the Roman educational system. On most Sundays she still went to mass at the Church of Christ the King.

When she enrolled at Rome University, she found some of the leaders of the "movement" who had impressed her at Mamiani High. One was the dark, brooding son of poor immigrants from Calabria. Claudio, two years her senior, was a firebrand during the interminable discussions of the "collective," but was taciturn in private. Even when Claudio and Simona were dating, he apparently didn't talk much to her. Neither of the two had a degree, let alone a job, but they got married anyway. Simona's mother, who disapproved, insisted on a church wedding and wept throughout the ceremony. She permitted the young couple to live in one of her apartments that had just become vacant, the place near the Piazza Vittorio.

Claudio was studying mathematics and said he might become a high school teacher or a university instructor. He always seemed to have more money than students from workers' families normally have, and he explained that in addition to a government scholarship he had earnings from tutoring. Simona got regular allowances from her mother, and she and Claudio were able to live in modest comfort. They often went out and sometimes had friends in. The neighbors had no reason for complaints; there were no wild parties, just wine from the trattoria, bread and cheese, and plenty of quiet talk. Simona and Claudio had no children; she mentioned recently that she would like to have a baby someday.

I have never met Claudio, but from what I have heard about him from third persons I gather that he must live in a state of permanent rage. Even as a teenager he'd complained that because he was a southerner and the child of poor people he was always being discriminated against. He had good grades in high school and hit it off with a mathematics teacher, but had many arguments with other members of the teaching staff. For a year or so he was active in the Communist Party's youth federation, but soon dropped out to join more radical groups. He said the Italian Communist Party had gone soft, was no longer a revolutionary movement, and was making deals with the Christian Democrats. He used to repeat that "the Italian system is not to be changed, it is to be destroyed."

By the time Claudio started dating Simona he apparently was already a conspirator. He had a gun without a permit, and after they were married he told her he had taken part in bombings. He almost certainly got money from the clandestine organization that had earlier recruited him as a part-time activist. The funds were raised by "self-financing"— bank holdups, service station robberies, and raids on supermarkets and other businesses. Claudio may have participated in such actions.

It is hard for an outsider to say how much Simona knew of her husband's clandestine activities. She admired him and doubtless was greatly influenced by him, although she claims now that she was already a revolutionary in high school. One day Claudio left their apartment and disappeared. Simona told her mother he was no good, and there had been another woman. The mother happily informed friends and acquaintances that Simona's marriage hadn't worked out, as she had always predicted, and that there would be a divorce. Actually, Simona is still legally married to Claudio, although nobody seems to know—except maybe she—where he is living and what has become of him. He hasn't seen his parents for years and hasn't collected his study grant money. Many young people have vanished in Rome lately: some have gone to India on cheap flights and are shooting heroin in Goa; others are leading underground existences at home.

Claudio is probably a full-time plotter and a soldier of the "armed party," but he apparently hasn't been identified yet by the antiterrorism investigators. No policeman has ever made inquiries about him in the building off the Piazza Vittorio where he was living with his young wife, or at the miserable little house near Ciampino Airport that is still the home of his parents and their other children.

Simona did not graduate from the university, but instead took a training course for social workers and got the day-care job. If she ever sees her husband, which is quite possible, such meetings don't take place in her apartment. The guests who occasionally stay with her for a day or two are activists and couriers of the "armed party" who have to be put up in an unobtrusive way, Simona gave me to understand. The location of her place is ideal for that purpose. For one thing, it is very close to the Stazione Termini, the railroad terminal through which thousands of travelers pass every hour. It seems that terrorists move around the country a lot. They may come to the capital for some carefully planned action and then go off to Turin or Naples, or maybe even to France, to lie low for some time.

The fact that Simona's apartment is in the crowded Piazza Vittorio section is also an advantage. The outdoor market, Rome's biggest and reputedly cheapest, is supplied by truck farmers from a wide area around the capital and attracts shoppers from all over the city and the suburbs. Pickpockets, con men, shady characters of all kinds, Arabs, and Africans mingle with the market throng and loiter under the arcades around the square. It is a bazaar where one can easily disappear in the crowd.

Simona's occasional guests don't make a splash anyway. They are dressed like middle-class people, the men often looking like insurance company clerks, the women like her colleagues in the city services. Her visitors sometimes leave packages or suitcases with her that may contain guns, explosives, money, forged identity cards, or fake license plates to be put on stolen getaway cars before a robbery or armed attack. She admits she is always relieved when someone calls later to reclaim the hot stuff. Most of the time the police wouldn't find anything more revolutionary in her apartment than books by Che Guevara and Frantz Fanon and an article on urban guerrillas by Ulrike Meinhof. Simona doesn't even keep the copies of *Lotta Continua,* Rome's far-left daily, that she buys at various newsstands from time to time.

Simona asserts she hasn't actively participated in any violence since she tossed that Molotov cocktail during the anti-American protest. However, she does defend terrorism as the only way of bringing down, as she puts it, "the imperialist state of the multinationals." The phrase recurs in the leaflets that the Red Brigades disseminate after many of their murders.

Some of Simona's charges at the day-care center are the children of policemen. I asked her how she felt about the terrorist assassinations of badly paid Public Security or Carabinieri subalterns. "Tough luck," she said. "They have agreed to be mercenaries for the system. They are being

107

caught in the surge of history." Besides, she added, many policemen were torturing detained leftists and deserved to be dealt with ruthlessly.

Episodes of hardship or injustice that the parents of children in the day-care center tell Simona, the unending stream of scandals that she reads about in the newspapers, her own experiences with uncaring or bungling officials, the dismal conditions in schools and hospitals that everybody can see —all this continually feeds her indignation. For Simona, all the problems in Italy—the corruption, the privileges of the rich and powerful, inflation, crime—are evidence of a huge plot by the multinational companies, the Central Intelligence Agency of the United States, and their pawns in Italy to exploit the "proletariat" and keep it enslaved.

There isn't much of an authentic working class in Rome, I contended during one of many talks with Simona, pointing out that the city was rather parasitical from a socioeconomic point of view, and that Romans on the whole live much better than the people in any capital in the Communist orbit. She countered that the Italian model of a consumer society is imperialism's trick to keep the masses under control. She did, though, on occasion criticize the kind of Roman radicals who, she said, would dynamite police barracks and assassinate Carabinieri officers and judges from autumn to spring in order to live it up on the beaches of Calabria and Sardinia, or even on the French Riviera, in the hot months, spending the money they had amassed through supermarket holdups.

Where should all the terrorism lead to? I asked Simona several times in our discussions. She admitted that a large part of the "proletariat" didn't support the armed underground movement, and predicted that Italy would go through a period of harsh repression, maybe another Fascist dictatorship. Eventually, the people would rise up and the "proletariat" would take over, she said. When I insisted on knowing more about that ultimate phase in the terrorists' scheme of things to come, Simona was always vague. "Just let's destroy the system first," she kept repeating.

Is there any model in today's world for the kind of society that the Red Brigades and their allies want to build after their victory? I asked. Maybe in the Soviet Union, China, Cuba, Yugoslavia, Albania? All Simona would say was that the Italian solution would surely be a Communist system, but that it would be tailored to the country's own needs, incorporating features of other socialist societies.

On one point Simona is specific: the condition of women will be radically improved. She has long been interested in the feminist movement and has read much of its literature, though she doesn't belong to any organized group. She often says that women in Italy are twice exploited—by their own men and by the capitalist-imperialist establishment. She repeatedly told me that in the "armed party" women were playing a big role and often took part in commando actions. Several woman terrorists are in fact on the police's most wanted list. Simona herself is patently proud of contributing to the underground fight by giving shelter to terrorists.

She is one of thousands of anonymous and unsuspected Italians—surely there are hundreds in Rome alone—who actively prove their sympathy for the Red Brigades and other terrorist networks by acting as "moles" in offices and businesses where they gather useful information, and by rendering other services as "irregulars" or auxiliaries. Simona's husband has long been a "regular," or salaried full-time conspirator, and has probably been instrumental in maneuvering her, step by step, into her present dangerous position. It might be risky at this stage for Simona to refuse further services to the terrorists unless she went to live abroad, but apparently she has never thought of backing out.

Recently she applied for enrollment in a course that will train social assistants for the rehabilitation of lawbreakers. Her application will make sense to the authorities: with her three years as a psychology student and her good record at the day-care center, her wish to engage in rehabilitation work is plausible and her motivations are credible. But I suspect that in this move, as in other things, Simona is following orders from the underground.

When she asked to be admitted to the training course, she mentioned that she might use her new experiences to finish her psychology studies and then graduate. Actually, Simona wants access to prisoners. She would be very useful to the "armed party" as a courier between the underground and jailed terrorists. Italy's prisons are indeed one of the three reservoirs from which the Red Brigades and kindred clandestine groups draw much of their strength. The other two are schools and the anarchist fringes of workers in big industrial plants.

Although suspected and convicted terrorists are theoretically being held separately, contacts with other inmates in Italy's overcrowded prisons are frequent. The "armed party" often manages to enlist recruits among common criminals. Terrorists and ordinary offenders have joined forces in many jailbreaks.

I told Simona I had a fairly good idea why she wanted to make prison visits, but did she realize the tremendous risks she was taking? Her brown eyes became hard. "I have chosen my place," she declared edgily. "It is with the struggling proletariat."

STUDENT BACKLASH

Something new is going on at Mamiani High, the high school where Simona got her indoctrination. Maybe it's the beginning of a backlash against the turbulence of the education system. It seems that students want to learn more than they have during the last several restless years. They demand that their teachers transmit more relevant knowledge about the present-day world. They request that programs in economics and sociology be added to the antiquated curriculum, that school libraries be replenished, and that faculty members bring themselves up to date on the latest developments in their fields. Many teachers aren't too happy about this novel trend.

The high school on the Viale delle Milizie has for years been a breeding ground for radicalism, as have most other teaching institutions. The outer walls of the complex at the border between the city's Prati and delle Vittorie sections are always covered with extremist graffiti. Truculent slogans are often spray-painted in the corridors and classrooms or chalked on the blackboards. When students go to classes in the morning, far-left activists clustered at the gate hand them leaflets denouncing "imperialism" or the "revisionism" of the Italian Communist Party.

It is a rare day when all 1,100 students show up; many cut their classes most of the time. Tension in the school has risen during the last few years between leftist students and others who were active in the neofascist underground, a group that has a stronghold in the middle-class Prati section.

"Prati is black!" proclaim slogans painted on many walls. It's not the black of priestly cassocks, but that of Mussolini's Blackshirts. Reds and blacks often clash in neighborhood street battles, and youngsters from Mamiani High are usually among them. Some time ago, a Greek student who had joined the neofascist militants was killed in a fight on the nearby Piazza Risorgimento.

Now the Mamiani has become the base of a new group that calls itself the Democratic Federative Movement and has started a citywide campaign for better education. The student leaders of the movement describe themselves as Roman Catholics who identify with left-wing causes. In collaboration with the youth federation of the Communist Party and a group to its left, the young school reformers worked up a manifesto and questionnaire that they disseminated in Mamiani and other Roman high schools. The response was prompt and encouraging—ten thousand students answered the questions.

The teaching staff at the Mamiani, dominated by leftists, rejected the student demands in a straw vote, thirty-one to seven. A statement by the majority contended that the student movement appeared to accept the "basic mechanisms" of capitalist society and betrayed a deplorable desire for "efficiency and productivity." The wording echoed the ultraleftist thesis that the school system, like other structures of the capitalist society, is so rotten that it cannot be improved but must be destroyed altogether.

One of the seven members of the faculty who sided with the student movement in the straw vote, Attilio Mariani, is the school's principal. He says he views the student demands as an attempt to "come to grips with utopia," the radical ideas of 1968. That was the year of the French student revolt, which quickly spilled into Italy and for several years kept its schools in turmoil. The upheaval was particularly violent in Rome.

At Mamiani High and other schools, militant far-left students have for years been fighting for the "political six," or automatic passing grades. Degrees of accomplishment in Italian schools are from zero, meaning utter failure, to 10, which indicates a seldom-reached excellence; a 6 is the minimum for passing an exam. The battle for the "political six" stemmed from the radical argument that since the existing school system must be demolished, students engaged in this revolution should not be bothered with examinations.

The guaranteed passing grades were never officially sanctioned, but in practice, the public school system came rather close to accepting the ultraleftist demand that teachers should not commit further injustices by flunking participants in a cultural revolution. High school programs were revised so as to do away with what is called *nozionismo,* or "notionism," a new Italian word that means, with overtones of contempt, the accumulation of mere notions, or useless knowledge. The despised notions are the names of emperors, kings, and popes, and the years when they reigned, the dates of historical battles, the conjugation of Latin and Greek verbs, mathematical formulas, geographical data, verses from Dante and Ariosto, and all the many other things that Italian high school students once used to learn by rote and were expected to recite in exams.

Since 1968, the Ministry of Public Instruction in countless circulars has directed teachers to take into consideration the entire personality, mental processes, and commitment of students, not just their performance in a specific test. Thus "notionism" was officially disavowed, and young scholars could expect to be promoted even if they couldn't name the year when the battle of Cannae was fought or recall the capital of Norway.

"Our students don't have time to pick up many notions even if they wanted to," a middle-aged teacher at Mamiani High told me. "According to the law, there should be 215 days of school during the academic year, fewer than in almost all other European countries, but even that modest target is never met." The teacher explained: "School officially starts in the second half of September, but actually it doesn't. Weeks go by before professors are definitely assigned and schedules have been worked out. There is such disorder in our school system. All the time I have to substitute for colleagues who don't show up; it may be November before I can remember the names of my own pupils, if they care to attend classes. Then there are often strikes by teacher unions or by students. And Christmas and Easter vacations."

The teacher noted that by late May there is already a general end-of-term atmosphere and that every other year or so the government closes the schools prematurely because it needs the classrooms for an election. Italy has been a democracy since 1945 but still has no other places for polling stations than the schools. Recalling the upheaval in the Roman education system after 1968, the teacher at the Mamiani said: "All the time groups of youngsters, not always from our school, would burst into the classroom asking my students to join some assembly, parade, or rally. The kids would use vile language—and still do—or attack professors. Several of my colleagues no longer take their cars to school, or they look for parking space far away, for fear that hostile students will wreck the autos. Some of my friends have taken early retirement because they just couldn't cope with the chaos in the schools. Now it's a little calmer. The wildest youngsters have grown up, maybe become terrorists and gone underground. The saddest thing, in my view, is that ambitious kids who are intelligent and want to study are mocked, despised, often beaten up."

A student at Mamiani High who takes learning seriously and wants to become an ecologist said: "My main complaint is the rapid turnover of professors. We get the substitute for a substitute for a substitute. Last year we counted nine different professors in Italian Literature class alone. About every week another young guy came, told the class that we are immature and don't know anything, joked with the girls, and was never seen again." Education officials admit that the entire school system is plagued by bad staff discipline, in addition to the chronic student unrest. Teachers assigned to a class report in sick and through their own connections obtain transfers to more desirable positions. An army of frustrated substitute teachers who are denied tenure drift from class to class and from school to school.

The mess in the public institutions prompts many parents to send their children to private schools, most of them operated by Roman Catholic teaching orders, and some run by foreign groups with instruction in English, French, or German. About 15 percent of all young Romans on the elementary and secondary levels attend nonpublic institutions at considerable cost to their families. The priests, friars, and nuns who teach in the parochial schools know that many of their pupils' fathers carry Communist Party membership cards.

In the poll conducted by the new student group at Mamiani High, 83 percent of those who filled in the questionnaire reported that their teachers had never mentioned such things as how one looks for a job by first registering with the labor exchange, or what the rights of Italian workers are. The Mamiani movement demands, among other things, that the schools prepare students for the practical and social problems of today's world.

The high schools in Rome and all of Italy currently produce unprepared and low-quality college students. Graduation after eight years of secondary instruction is almost automatic now and guarantees admittance to any institution of higher learning. Before 1968, the so-called maturity examination, a set of demanding tests at the end of high school, was a dreaded ordeal that years later would continue to haunt the nightmares of anyone who had gone through it—much like the *baccalauréat* in France. The campaign against "notionism" has considerably lowered the last hurdle before college, making the examinations for the graduation certificate almost a pushover. The Italian graduation certificate is a piece of paper needed for medium-level bureaucratic careers and for admittance to a university. Since there are few openings in the job market unless one has an Uncle Annibale or some other patron—a "saint in paradise"—most graduates go right on to college without having to worry about entrance requirements. The campus of Rome State University was built under Mussolini for, at most, 20,000 students; the institution now has an enrollment of 150,000.

Lack of space for students in classrooms, seminars, the library, and the laboratories makes the mammoth university an anthill. The ants are thoroughly politicized. Neofascists are strong in law school, while Marxists dominate the physics department. The architecture school is in the hands of ultraleftists. In all departments, most of the teaching and supervision of laboratory work is done by instructors and assistant professors who resent the power of the "barons," the tenured incumbents of the professorial chairs. The untouchable "barons" put in rare appearances on campus, preferring to make money in private practice or as consultants to government or big business. Under such conditions it is quite possible to enroll in medical school while holding down a desk job in a ministry and to prepare for the anatomy exam from mimeographed notes that add to the income of some "baron."

There are no dormitories on the campus of Rome State University, and precious few vacancies in the handful of student hostels around the city. Most of the university students live with their parents, some of them in cities and towns far away from the capital. There are many absentees, who show up only for registration and exams. Some branches of the giant Rome University, like the engineering department, have managed, thanks to the devotion of individual professors and instructors, to maintain high standards. Others do little research and have in effect become factories turning out doctors' diplomas.

The degrees of Rome University are of little value on the job market today. A doctor of philosophy—in most cases a graduate in letters and humanities—may seek to win an assignment as a substitute high school teacher; a doctor of law will bone up for the bar exam or apply for a post in government or "subgovernment." The more substantive degrees—in medicine, the natural sciences, mathematics—are evaluated by prospective employers like fine wines: the good Roman vintages were before 1968, but there may be new ones in store if the student backlash reaches higher learning.

Right now big corporations hiring applicants for technical jobs prefer candidates with foreign degrees. Sometimes they send homegrown graduates to training courses given by foreign affiliates. Much of Rome State University might as well operate in an underdeveloped country—an enormous student body, a surfeit of politics, frequent unrest and occasional violence, little academic work, even less scientific research, and plenty of parchments with fancy and worthless doctor's titles.

The dismal rating of higher education in the Italian capital is exemplified by a brass sign that has just been put up at a house entrance in the Vicolo del Bottino, a side street off the fashionable Spanish Square. The message is common in Third World cities, but in so demonstrative a manner new for Rome. The sign reads: "Dr. M. Ghotbi. Internal Medicine. Graduate of Berlin University."

BUREAUCRATIC
UNDERBRUSH

Norma is one of the medical students enrolled at Rome State University who never attends classes there. Instead, she is on the staff of the Ministry of Industry, Commerce, and Handicrafts. She has her own office in the ministry, where she memorizes mimeographed lecture texts she has bought from her professors. She is confident that they will enable her to pass her tests and to reach her goal of becoming a physician.

She isn't the only absentee student at the university, nor is she the only worker in the ministry who uses government offices to pursue personal sidelines. Some sell baby clothes, bedspreads, and knitwear to fellow workers; others run building cooperatives from their desks. The Industry Ministry, all other government departments, and the luxuriant jungle of semigovernmental agencies in Rome are full of people who seem to have little or nothing to do in their jobs while a small minority of personnel on the public payroll is overworked.

Still, it seems odd to the unshaved receptionist-messenger at one end of the corridor outside Norma's office when Norma's mother begins to show up every day. Apparently the mother, a widow, has been feeling lonely at home. She sits in a corner in Norma's office, often doing needlework, while the future doctor studies anatomy texts. Who has arranged permission for this? Norma or her mother must be under the protection of some powerful personage. A minister? A cardinal? The other employees on the floor and the receptionist-messenger greet the two women respectfully.

Apart from the daughter-mother office, it's a typical ministerial floor. The work day begins at eight A.M., and an hour later most officials are actually at their desks. At nine A.M. sharp the doorkeeper downstairs folds the check-in lists in which all those who have reported for duty signed their names and takes it to the personnel section. If you are more than an hour late, you might as well stay home unless you care to walk into the personnel chief's office and explain meekly that you had a domestic crisis because your younger child is running a fever, or that the No. 56 bus broke down and you were stranded for half an hour on your way to work.

Office hours end at two P.M., but on Saturday, a working day in many branches of the government, employees start going home at one. The theoretical thirty-six-hour week, from eight A.M. to two P.M. Mondays through Saturdays, was introduced under Mussolini as a privilege for the capital's bureaucracy and has proved much more resistant than the Fascist system. Government workers in the provinces, who always had to spend more time in their offices than their envied Roman colleagues, repeatedly demanded the extra-short work schedule for themselves too, but the central authorities and the nation's courts turned them down.

Norma may not be doing anything to promote industry, commerce, and the handicrafts, but at least she is at her desk all the time. Many of her colleagues disappear for hours soon after they have signed in. Some go to have a leisurely breakfast at the in-house coffee shop, others walk over to the Bar Arizona just outside the massive travertine palace that Mussolini built to house his Ministry of Corporations.

It is a normal morning at the ministry if half the staff on Norma's floor are in their offices. Some haven't shown up at all and have phoned in around ten A.M. that they don't feel well. Sickness is likely to strike especially on Mondays and whenever it rains. A government employee who claims to be ill has to submit a medical certificate only after three days' consecutive absence. It is of course easy to find a doctor who will write out such a note.

The chief of a section at the Foreign Ministry told me: "I never know whether my secretary will turn up or phone she is down with a cold or tell me some other excuse for not coming to work. She is charming but completely unreliable." The Foreign Ministry is housed in the Palazzo della Farnesina, a megalomaniacal structure near Mussolini's sports forum on the right bank of the Tiber River that was not yet finished when the dictatorship collapsed. Democratic Italy not only completed the huge construction project, which rivals the United States Department of State in Washington, but managed also to fill it with a number of diplomats and support staff worthy of a superpower. But the marble corridors of the Foreign Ministry often look deserted.

An official of the Food and Agriculture Organization, an agency of the United Nations system that has its headquarters in what was meant to become Mussolini's Africa Ministry near the Circus Maximus, drove to the Italian Ministry of Agriculture one morning to request some information. The Italian civil servant with whom he was supposed to meet wasn't in. "What's more," the FAO expert told me, "the entire floor of the ministry seemed abandoned, as if a fire drill had just taken place. The doors to some offices were open, but nobody was inside. From the end of the corridor a radio was blaring. It was eerie."

If little is done in many government departments in the morning, some activity starts between five and six P.M. Several of Norma's colleagues, one third to a half of the entire staff, come back to their offices after a long, late lunch break and actually grapple with their work backlogs. They are all on overtime. To put in extra hours at extra pay is a way of rounding out one's income and beating inflation; it has become an almost automatic privilege that goes with a government job in Rome. However, some members of the ministry staff don't want to work overtime because they have found better-paying occupations, maybe as consultants to firms that have dealings with the administration.

The official in the corner room on the floor above Norma's always seems to be at his desk. He comes in at eight A.M., often stays long after two P.M., goes to the luncheonette on the Piazza Barberini for a bite, is back before four P.M., and stays late. He bears the title counselor, has a law degree from the University of Bari, and is a chain smoker. He virtually runs an entire section of the ministry by himself. He earns plenty on overtime and surely needs the money for his family of five. His wife and three children see little of him during the week, and there is a suspicion that he takes work home over weekends. The personal secretary to the industry minister often calls the counselor into his office to give him special assignments. His colleagues call him the *fanatico.* In Rome, the word doesn't really mean a fanatic but something like "pedantic workaholic," and is usually uttered with the contempt reserved for cuckolds.

The *fanatico* is in fact a pillar of the Industry Ministry. If there weren't a few devoted bureaucrats like him in the building, the entire department would be paralyzed. There are similar figures scattered in other government services. Whatever their personal motivations, they do not only their own work but also that of many others. Somehow they keep Rome's creaky and cumbersome administrative machinery working. It functions badly enough anyway.

For instance, a Roman who takes a driving test usually has to wait for three or four months before the driver's license is issued. And the waiting time may be ten years for somebody entitled to a pension; until the exact amount is eventually fixed, one has to manage with cash advances and hope to live long enough to receive all the back payments. Electronic data processing in the government services hasn't quickened the glacial pace of the Roman bureaucracy. "The computer has broken down," has become a standard explanation whenever a citizen complains. In truth, the government lacks the programmers and knowhow to make the expensive hardware function.

The *fanatico* in the Industry Ministry often sighs, as do his opposite numbers in other branches of the administration, that he is surrounded by incompetent and lazy people. His department has many dealings with the Brussels headquarters of the European Economic Community, but every time some letter or circular in French, English, or German arrives, there is a crisis. A French communication provides Norma's great moment, because she knows a little French and can help out. When Roman government offices need translations, they often have to enlist outside interpreters. But even normal office routines seem to present difficulties. The other day I held a memo from the prime minister in my hands; it contained several typing errors, some corrected, others not, and a misspelled word. One recent evening the government chief was forced to peck out the draft for an official statement himself because no typist could be found in the entire Palazzo Chigi at that hour.

The incompetence, absenteeism, waste, and abysmal level of productivity in the Roman government apparatus have long been a national scandal, deepening the disaffection that Italians in the provinces feel toward their capital. Since 1954, each of the many cabinets that have followed one another has included a minister in charge of doing something about the inert monster. The department that the successive ministers built up was first called the Ministry of the Bureaucratic Reform, then the Ministry of the Reform of the Public Administration, and eventually, with bashful blandness, the Ministry of the Civil Service.

Political leaders and experts agree that all timid attempts at revamping the bureaucratic mechanisms have so far been futile. The leisurely bumbling of the Roman civil service is in part a legacy from the age-old work habits of the papal Curia, which itself is heir to the majestic slowness and legal quibbling that characterized the administrative machinery of the Byzantine and Roman emperors. Curial ponderousness has been proverbial through the centuries. Recent popes abolished some antiquated routines and increased the strength of the non-Italian personnel in the Vatican, yet in its methods and outlook the Curia has to this day remained essentially Italianate.

In the Vatican, too, there are a few officials in daily contact with the Pope or his chief aides who work very hard and put in long hours. This is true particularly of the more than one hundred prelates and officials of the Secretariat of State, the Curia's power center. They seem even physically to be distinct from other priests—better groomed, a kind of clerical elegance in speech and manners, an elite. However, despite recent "reforms of the Curia," maybe more thorough than those of the Roman government bureaucracy, many Vatican prelates and their staffs still dawdle in sleepy offices in the morning and can't be found in the afternoon. Whenever members of the church hierarchy at large have a chance of meeting, they lament the Roman Curia's slowness in decision making. Cardinals from abroad who took part in the secret conclaves that led to the elections of Pope John Paul I and Pope John Paul II in 1978 complained vocally about the sluggish and high-handed procedures of the Italian-dominated Curia.

The Vatican at least produces an organization chart every January. It is the red-bound *Annuario Pontificio,* or pontifical yearbook, which in its more than a thousand pages lists all the Sacred Congregations, offices, tribunals, secretariats, commissions, and other bodies that make up the Roman Curia. Characteristically, it is issued in Italian only. There is no such reliable guide for Rome's secular bureaucracy.

This lack is particularly felt by those who must penetrate the weird underbrush of semigovernmental agencies that the Italians call their *sottogoverno,* or subgovernment. It reaches from the colossal Italian Hydrocarbons Authority (ENI), with a work force of 120,000, to a maze of innumerable, half-forgotten offices tucked away in rented quarters in various Roman apartment houses.

ENI, which supplies the nation with more than half the oil and natural gas it needs, and is headquartered in a concrete-and-glass high-rise building in Rome's World Fair district, was once a state within the state. In the 1950s, the fuel authority through its network of agents abroad, especially in the Middle East, conducted international relations of its own that often deviated from Italy's official pro-Western foreign policy line. In Iran or Libya, the Italian ambassador would do or say one thing, the resident ENI representative another. Usually ENI had its way. At home, too, ENI wielded immense political influence and funds. However, the fuel authority failed to develop substantial oil fields in Italy or abroad, and today must buy from producer countries almost all the crude oil its refineries swallow. ENI's first chief, the forceful and controversial Enrico Mattei, died in an air crash in 1962; since then the oil-and-gas empire has lost much of its former clout and has become both the object and the arena of infighting between rival political factions.

Another forbidding thicket in the Roman subgovernment is the social security system, with clusters of agencies that wastefully and inefficiently administer the nation's health care and old-age benefits. One of the most coveted plums in the *sottogoverno* is a high-level job at RAI, the state broadcasting network that has spawned a bureaucracy of an especially backbiting variety. The most bizarre spots in the Roman subgovernment are small bureaucratic bodies that quietly vegetate on public funds without rendering any tangible service to the community.

This boscage thrives in the shade of anonymity. Parliament and various governments repeatedly start drives against what are known as the "useless agencies," trying to cut the rankest and most wasteful growths. Among them was an office that had once been set up to take care of the orphans of World War II, and which was still in existence at a time when the youngest of them were in their thirties, old enough to look after themselves.

Despite the attempted cleanup, there are still scores,

maybe hundreds, of "institutes," "centers," and "agencies" all over Rome that occupy a few dusty rooms and pretend to foster relations with Latin America, promote the cultivation of hemp or silk, or conduct research into medieval history or African ethnology. Employees drop in whenever they feel like it, make a few private phone calls, maybe edit a bulletin or periodical that will find few readers, pay themselves salaries out of the government subsidies, and are careful not to rock the boat.

Add to the government and sprawling subgovernment the separate bureaucracies of the political parties, the trade unions, and the big banks. Include also the missions that business concerns in the industrial north maintain in the capital for liaison with national power centers. The grand total is 600,000 office workers in a city with a population of 3 million —the bulk of the regular labor force in a community where innumerable residents have no definable job and live by hazy "arrangement." The army of bureaucrats looks overwhelming compared with the 100,000 industrial workers that the Roman metropolitan area employs, and the between 10,000 and 20,000 unskilled and semiskilled hands that find work in the building trades.

The figures reveal that bureaucracy is by far Rome's most important pursuit. It would be unjust to assert that all of the city's 600,000 office workers are drones. The men and women behind the windows at the post offices—besieged by droves of impatient and quarrelsome people who want to pay their electricity bills—certainly earn their salaries. But in Roman offices there are far too many Normas of both sexes, and few of them are studying to become doctors.

HOSPITAL LOCKOUT

One day in 1980, suddenly, without any warning, Rome's
major public hospitals refused to admit new patients. Red
Cross ambulances carrying people in need of medical care
had to tour the city for hours before an empty bed could be
found in some private institution. Several sick people had to
be taken to hospitals in Frascati, Albano, and other towns in
the hills southeast of Rome. What was happening?

I went out to the San Giovanni Hospital, a medical complex near the Lateran some of whose buildings date from the
seventeenth century. The institution has a capacity of close
to a thousand patients but was crammed with almost half
again that many. Beds were lined up end to end in sour-
smelling corridors, waiting rooms, and administration
offices. The day before, angry patients and nurses had
banded together, throwing hospital beds out of windows
and carrying them into the street to demonstrate against
overcrowding and poor conditions.

One of the senior doctors, Professor Luciano Persico,
said, "Whenever I want a patient to clean up, I sign a temporary dismissal slip for a few hours enabling him or her to go
home and take a shower." Facilities in the San Giovanni were
inadequate and often filthy. The twenty patients lying in one
long corridor had a single toilet, and it was flooded. "Mice
and rats in the kitchen, cockroaches under the beds," said a
diabetes patient with a broken leg.

A few months earlier, a cancer patient in the Policlinico
Hospital, which adjoins Rome State University, had been

besieged by a swarm of ants. During the night the ants had gotten into his throat. Local newspapers reported the scandalous case. The news was picked up abroad, and the West German mass-circulation daily *Bild* carried a fat headline across its entire front page reading CANCER PATIENT DEVOURED BY ANTS. *Bild* relishes such stories.

In addition to public hospitals, Rome has a few very good medical institutions; they are run by private operators and religious orders and are quite expensive. When former Prime Minister Giulio Andreotti had to have a gall bladder operation, he entered the Villa Stuart clinic on Monte Mario, where German nuns are in charge. It is fashionable in Rome to have babies delivered in the maternity ward of Salvator Mundi International Hosptial on the Janiculum, with American and Asian sisters of the Salvatorian order in attendance.

A friend of mine took his sick wife out of a clinic run by a community of friars on the Via Cassia and had her transferred to the Salvator Mundi after she complained to him that the doctor in charge was always examining her with a cigarette dangling from his mouth, the ashes dropping on her bed.

An official in a government department whose wife was suffering from a kidney disease took her to the university hospital at Louvain, Belgium, and said that the treatment—which was successful—came to less, travel expenses included, than it would have cost him in a private clinic here. Romans requiring major surgery or intensive care who can afford the expenditure often go to hospitals in Switzerland or the United States.

For Romans who couldn't travel to Zurich to be admitted to the Cantonal Hospital, or who couldn't pay the stiff fees at a private institution, the hospital closing was especially difficult. The situation was "worrisome," the health commissioner of the Rome regional government allowed. The hospital lockout, which was said to be "unofficial" but was nevertheless effective, seemed to have developed quickly when the directors of three or four major medical centers telephoned the Red Cross to advise that their facilities were strained to the breaking point and to suggest that ambulances should take sick people to some place other than theirs.

Rome's public hospitals have together about twenty thousand beds for a population that is officially set at close to 3 million. Actually, at least 1.5 million more who live within commuting distance from the city also depend to a large extent on the capital's medical institutions. Furthermore, many patients arrive from southern Italy because they need treatment that they can't get there, or because they don't trust their local hospitals.

Officials also blamed the hospital crisis on the undeniable fact that many beds are occupied indefinitely by patients who really ought to be in old people's homes. Families who can't or won't care for an elderly, ailing relative always seem to find some doctor to diagnose a chronic disease enabling them to park Grandfather or Auntie in a general hospital.

What's more, many mentally disturbed persons had recently been admitted to Roman public hospitals and were being treated indiscriminately with other patients instead of in special psychiatric wards. Several of the mental cases were former inmates of St. Mary of Pity, the old lunatic asylum on Monte Mario; they had been dismissed from it under new legislation aimed at reducing the number of persons committed to such institutions.

There was another new category of patients in the city's public hospitals: drug addicts. Despite the alarming proportions the narcotics problem had lately assumed, Rome still lacked a specialized center for the treatment and rehabilitation of addicts. The presence of drug cases among other patients in the general hospitals, sometimes in the same wards, had increased the disorder in the institutions. At the Policlinico, patients had staged protests and written to newspapers, charging that the drug addicts had brought with them into the hospital a flourishing narcotics traffic and were responsible for a wave of thefts and occasional violence.

In Rome, doctors, nurses, and other hospital personnel are periodically on strike for a variety of reasons. Often managers of medical complexes here have to send out for sandwiches to feed patients—many of them on special diets —because the kitchen staffs have walked out. In some Roman hospitals it has become routine for the relatives of patients to take bed sheets home for laundering because they are only infrequently changed by the personnel.

When the lockout occurred, the press decried the "chaos" in Rome's hospitals. Yet the conditions seem to be as chronic as the liver infections in certain unhealthy neighborhoods of the city, particularly in the shantytowns along the Aniene River, a tributary of the Tiber that ecologists have long denounced as an "open sewer."

The lockout came just as Italy's new national health service was to go into effect. The long-debated reform was meant to assure free medical treatment and hospital care to all Italians. But from the official start of the new program at the beginning of the year it was bedeviled by red tape, inefficiency, and general cynicism. "The national health service will go from ill-starred birth to irreversible coma," said one of the country's many medical associations. Not surprisingly, physicians were among the fiercest opponents of the reform, which was intended to supersede a maze of health insurance bodies that left many people without any medical coverage at all.

Tens of thousands of Romans scrambled to register with one of the new, understaffed local health units and name their "physician of confidence." These chosen doctors, usually picked at random from an official list, are supposed to deal with general medical problems and refer patients to specialists as necessary. The services are in theory free, but virtually all specialists continue charging their usual fees.

Critics of the new program pointed out that the government blueprint called for ten layers of bureaucracy to make the national health service work, and contended that Italy had neither the financial resources nor the medical facilities to run such a ponderous apparatus with any chance of success.

Politicians and experts in Rome have been talking about urgent social reforms ever since the collapse of Mussolini's dictatorship. The need for better health services and better hospitals has for many years been given high priority. Yet the ramshackle characteristics of most of the existing institutions would make it advisable to improve the infrastructure before launching broad reforms.

A prestigious surgeon who heads a university clinic here, Professor Paride Stefanini, says the much-vaunted reform of health care "is made of good intentions only." He notes that the medical structures are inadequate and predicts that it might take ten years before any concrete results may be expected from the national health service. Meanwhile, he warns, things may get worse instead of better. The politicians, the labor leaders, and the physicians as a class all bear their share of responsibility for the present mess, Professor Stefanini thinks. He says it would have been wiser to start with a reform of the education system to train better nurses and doctors.

THE JOYS OF
THE SIESTA

The Italian ambassador who for nearly ten years was posted in Northern Europe and Canada was recently reassigned to the Foreign Ministry in Rome. He would be serving for at least three years in his nation's capital before he could expect to be given another job abroad, and he wasn't very happy about being home again. He would have to manage without the generous funds that sweeten the life of Italian diplomats in foreign countries. He complained that Rome isn't really interested in international affairs. He found his department disorganized and its staff rent by political factions and bureaucratic cliques. And he said that living conditions in the city had sadly deteriorated since he'd started his service career here.

"The only advantage is, I can again have a siesta," the ambassador remarked. "I missed it badly all these years. I never got really used to working or having official talks right after lunch."

Currently, the ambassador, who heads a department section, is one of the first officials to show up in the morning at the huge Palazzo della Farnesina; he is often at his desk before nine. He reads service dispatches, attends meetings, sees foreign diplomats, has a quick espresso, is called in to his immediate chief or even to the department's secretary-general, and at one P.M., on days when he does not have an official luncheon, he drives to his home in the Flaminio district on the opposite side of the Tiber.

But even when he does have an engagement, he makes sure he is in his apartment by three or three-thirty at the latest. Within minutes he is in bed. The shutters are closed and he dozes off at once. His nap may take forty-five minutes or an hour.

When he gets up, he drinks a cup of strong espresso that his wife insists on preparing herself, and at around five he returns to the Foreign Ministry. It's his best time for working. He writes reports, makes telephone calls to Italian embassies in the Western Hemisphere, where it is morning now, drafts circulars, and formulates recommendations for government action. Just before eight he rushes home to pick up his wife, changes into formal dress if required, and proceeds to the inevitable diplomatic reception, which may be followed by a dinner party. Late in the evening, at home, he studies nonclassified papers that he has brought from the office, makes entries in a diary that one day may become a book, and does some reading until after midnight.

"I am convinced that people who have the siesta habit work more and better than those who stick to the nine-to-five time frame," the ambassador likes to say. Most Romans agree with him, regardless of whether they themselves can indulge in an after-lunch snooze or not, and although they may think that working more and better isn't the most important thing in life.

Ask any native of the city or any longtime resident and you will be told that the siesta refreshes body and mind for an active and enjoyable second half of the day, that it staves off heart attacks and holds a promise of longevity, and that it's great for one's sex life. I have heard such praise of the siesta many times, in the most eloquent manner, from a lawyer who was a slave to the habit. He would accept invitations to business lunches with clients only if he were assured that within five minutes after the meal he could stretch out in a dark, quiet room in their home or at some place near the restaurant where they were to meet. Even such an arrangement was a hardship for him, though, because after lunch he hankered for his own bed and said he used to get undressed as if he were going to get a good night's sleep. His siesta often lasted more than two hours.

I asked one of Rome's leading heart specialists, Dr. Vittorio Puddu, what he thought about the health aspects of the siesta. A past president of the Italian Cardiac Society, Professor Puddu said that "nobody so far has studied the effect of the siesta on the heart." However, he added, he personally believed that the habit "is a good idea, especially in a warm climate and for people who lead stressful, fatiguing lives." I reminded the professor that the after-lunch nap had advocates in America, too, and that after his cardio-circulatory accidents President Eisenhower had been advised by Paul Dudley White, the renowned Boston heart specialist, to take a rest every afternoon. "Professor White was enamored of Italy and Italian life-styles," said Professor Puddu with a chuckle. "I knew him well. Whenever he came here, he took siestas, but he didn't do so at home."

During the last few years an increasing number of Romans, particularly white-collar workers and other wage earners, have been forced to give up their after-lunch shut-eye. But at two P.M. a hush still settles on the city. All stores close at one or one-thirty and won't reopen before four or four-thirty, groceries not before five-thirty. Officials in government departments who go to lunch at two won't be back at their desks—on overtime—before five, if they return at all. The habitual Roman noise abates. Traffic throughout the city becomes light, and motorists may even find parking spaces.

Few natives are seen in the streets at siesta time, and they are likely to look dejected. At construction sites, bricklayers munch huge sandwiches, then stretch out under the scaffolding and snore. Traffic policemen disappear from intersections that are no longer busy. Service stations close down for three hours. Half-empty buses run at long intervals.

Pickpockets rest up for the evening crush. In residential buildings everywhere in the city, venetian blinds are closed and shutters lowered.

The drivers of the fifty horse-drawn cabs that have survived in the city look for a spot in the shade near St. Peter's or in the Spanish Square and pull their caps over their eyes while their horses sleep on the hoof. However, man and beast may be rudely aroused from their slumber by some foreign tourists who insist on being shown the sights in the empty hours of early afternoon. "Mad dogs and Englishmen go out in the midday sun," Noel Coward wrote. "Englishmen detest the siesta." Romans abhor midday activity.

The imperative need for taking it easy after lunch has doubtless something to do with Roman eating patterns, although it is difficult to tell what is cause and what effect. Most people in the city breakfast on just a *cappuccino* and a sweet roll and are so hungry by the time they sit down for lunch that they wolf down the pasta heaped on their plate, following it with a meat or fish course and maybe topping it all with fruit or dessert, everything washed down by a few glasses of wine. Small wonder they feel drowsy afterward. Dinner is often lighter than lunch.

The city still has four rush hours on working days—in the morning; between one and two P.M., when many thousands hurry home for lunch and a snooze; around four, when some trudge back to their jobs; and after seven. However, although all retail stores and many offices still provide ample midday breaks for their employees, an increasing number of them live so far from their place of work that they can't make the round trip twice a day.

To cater to the swelling ranks of Romans who must get through their day without a siesta, many espresso places during the 1970s put up a new sign, SNACK BAR, and branched out into the fast-food business. The mood in such places between one and three P.M., when bank clerks and sales personnel crowd the counter to eat standing up, is strikingly different from the cheerful noise at all other hours.

134

Lunch in the espresso bar is a joyless affair. Patrons feed sullenly, then wander aimlessly around the deserted streets and piazzas of the neighborhood until it is time to go back to their jobs. When businesses and offices reopen in the afternoon, the atmosphere is palpably heavy with the drowsiness and bad temper of employees who couldn't take a nap. It will be five o'clock before Rome is alert again and gets a few things done.

The ecclesiastical establishment also divides its day into two distinct halves. Priests generally get up much earlier than do most other Romans, and are addicted to their midday nap. In the Vatican, too, everyone from the Pope to cardinals to doormen have traditionally dozed off after lunch, and many still do. But the Polish pontiff isn't used to the siesta, and his close aides must be prepared to be summoned to him, or receive phone calls from the papal suite, even during the once-hallowed rest period between three and five in the afternoon.

The Communist Party apparatus, on the other hand, is consistently Roman in its observance of the siesta. A delegation from the Hungarian Communist Party on an official visit not long ago was astonished to find only a few somnolent security guards at the Communist headquarters in the Via della Botteghe Oscure early one afternoon. All the other Italian comrades were out, and the word was they would be back after five. The business of international communism, like almost everything else in Rome, would have to pause till the siesta was over.

CONDOMINIUM ON
THE AVENTINE

Luisa is angry and worried. Ever since she and her husband arrived from a small town in the south eight or nine years ago she has been the *portiera,* the superintendent, of a condominium building on the Aventine. Now a majority of the apartment owners want her to leave. Luisa has already made two trips to labor union headquarters to find out whether she can be fired, and the answer seems to be yes.

A free apartment goes with the job. It consists of a tiny hall, a kitchen, a bedroom, and a toilet, all on one level between the ground floor and the basement. Not much of a place for a family of three—Luisa and her husband have a seven-year-old daughter—but she hopes they won't have to move.

The Aventine Hill, the plebeian quarter of ancient Rome, is today one of the city's choicest neighborhoods, fairly central and yet quiet because there is no through traffic. The other fourteen units in the building are of course much bigger than the super's, most of them with large terraces. The penthouse is outright fancy. The fragrance of jasmine and oleander shrubs in the small gardens between the street's villalike residential buildings wafts into the bedrooms. In the morning there is a concert of chirping birds. Unfortunately, every other household seems to be keeping a big dog as a burglar deterrent; on summer evenings the animals, excited by their mutual restlessness, often bark until late at night.

At the condominial council, the meeting of all apartment owners, the vote to let Luisa go came after a long discussion and was close. Nobody really wanted to get rid of her, and two or three people said it would be okay with them if Luisa wanted to stay on in the super's walkdown for the time being.

A widow whose late husband was a high official in the Education Ministry across the Tiber, and who herself is a retired high school teacher, told Luisa, "When you are no longer the *portiera,* why don't you help me in my apartment? I'd pay you the going rate." But Luisa doesn't want to be demoted to maid or cleaning woman.

Luisa is rather well liked. She used to do small favors for apartment owners, like taking in the widow's canaries when the former teacher (whom everybody calls *professoressa*) left for her annual cure in the spa of Fiuggi for a couple of weeks, or minding a baby while the mother hurried down to the pharmacy in the Viale Aventino. Every August, Luisa, her husband, and their little girl used to go to their hometown for a few days; when they came back she would bring a basketful of fresh figs and distribute them among the best tippers in the building.

People in the building rarely see Luisa's husband. Riccardo works as a bus driver for a travel bureau, and when he is at home he doesn't do anything for the building; he doesn't even replace burned-out light bulbs in the stairwell, let alone help Luisa wash the stairs or the windows. The regulars at a nearby espresso bar just off the Circus Maximus know him well—he likes to boast about his easy conquests of German and Swedish woman passengers on trips to Pompeii or Florence. Riccardo's reputation as a tourist-coach Casanova has trickled back; the people in the condominium feel sorry for Luisa and don't want to create more problems for her than she probably has already: while she is in her early thirties, she looks older, and it is said that she isn't very healthy and can't have any more children.

Why then is Luisa about to lose her job? The reason is money. The labor unions have just won another improvement in the mandatory contract terms for building superintendents that sharply increases their pay and gives women the same status as men. As a consequence, maintenance costs would almost double for the apartment owners on the Aventine who are Luisa's joint employers, and many of them say they can't afford such expenses. It is likely that another compulsory pay raise will come next year or the year after, and there is talk that the unions are about to push through a law providing that supers, where they still exist, cannot be dismissed at all, even if the intention is not to replace them.

The majority of unit owners in the building decided the only thing to do was to abolish the superintendent's job right now, pay off Luisa, keep the entrance door locked, and have an intercom system, a *citofono,* installed. Luisa is one of the last supers in the elegantly sloping and curving street; almost all the other apartment houses locked their entrances long ago.

Of course it is convenient to have a super who takes letters and packages from the mailman and distributes them in the building, calls the maintenance service when the elevator is once again stalled, can help out with a couple of eggs or a spoonful of salt, and keeps an eye on who goes in and out. However, during the recent long evening meeting in the fourth-floor apartment of the furniture dealer, several of the participants said yes, Luisa was a nice enough person, but the truth was that she was almost never to be seen in the little enclosure in the hallway, the *portineria.* The mailman would come, find nobody, and dump whatever he had to deliver on her little desk. Kids would come by and riffle through the mail before the addressees got it, if they got it at all. And as for burglaries, they guessed they had been lucky that nothing serious had happened, but it certainly wasn't because of

Luisa's presence—she often disappeared for hours. "And down at the number 16 building they still have a *portiere* who is a man, and you remember that night last summer when the thieves came with a van and without any fuss carted off all the Persian rugs from the apartment of the former ambassador who had just gone on vacation with his wife."

If Luisa deserts her post for hours at a time, the reason isn't that she has a secret life. It would be hard to lead one in a building with fifteen apartments whose occupants seem to know everything about one another, even though there are always a few who aren't on speaking terms after some quarrel over a dog that fouled the landing or a toy dropped from high up onto the ground-floor terrace.

Luisa is often absent because she is administering an injection to somebody stretched out on a couch or a bed in an apartment in the neighborhood. An astonishing volume of medical treatment in Italy consists of shots into the backsides of patients. The doctor prescribes two dozen fortifying injections for an adolescent who is listless in school or for a retiree who can't sleep, and advises that a nurse be found to give the shots. The packages with the vials are bought in the Viale Aventino pharmacy—the health-care system pays for them—and instead of calling a nurse, the patients' relatives turn to Luisa. She is deft with a syringe, stabs gently and precisely without hurting too much, and takes care to disinfect the area with alcohol. Luisa's mother was a midwife. Luisa herself has never had any paramedical training, but she even gives intravenous injections now and then, although doctors always warn that these should be done only by a registered nurse.

Although little is paid for the ten minutes it normally takes Luisa to give the shot, chat a little, and drink the espresso that now and then is offered to her, she must have saved some money. It is rumored that she is so angry now because she had planned to keep the super's job for, say, another five years before buying an apartment herself. Three times a year, at Christmas, Easter, and the midsummer holiday of

Ferragosto, Luisa used to receive at least a 10,000-lire note from every householder in the building. She got tips whenever she performed some special service such as taking up a big package to the actress on the third floor, who often gets flowers and other gifts, or buying newspapers and magazines for her. The actress liked this arrangement and tipped generously. People in the building tell each other when Luisa is out of earshot that the super's job, even with that no-good husband of hers, must have been a gold mine, what with all the tips and her flourishing practice as an unregistered nurse.

Maybe Luisa will be able to scratch together enough money for the down payment on an apartment in some popular condominium building in the suburbs—certainly not on the Aventine—and build a new practice with the syringe. Rome is covered with an invisible network of thousands of Luisas making the rounds and giving shots. Right now, she plans to hold out for a big severance pay and has consulted with the union lawyer on possible other claims. She has stopped greeting the apartment owners who voted for her dismissal, and has even stopped smiling at the widow with the canaries and at other people who voted in her favor. Supers don't attend condominial meetings, but Luisa has always been informed of everything that was said.

Luisa's sudden coolness even to her supporters in the building has brought about a shift in the mood. It seems likely that at the end of her upcoming three months' notice period, Luisa will have to relinquish the super's apartment. Under the condominium rules, the unit owners jointly own the super's flat, and several of them are already figuring out what their share will be when a new rent-paying tenant moves into the place. It won't be difficult to find one. There aren't many apartments for rent in Rome nowadays. Interest in Luisa's semi-basement is already keen.

For instance, a driver who works at the Cuban embassy around the corner would be happy to get it and would pay a good rental. He is an Italian and lives with his family somewhere on the far outskirts of the city, which forces him to get up very early to be at the embassy on time. He probably is a member of the Italian Communist Party, which wouldn't upset anyone, but his Cuban connection frightens some people. "With those Cubans, one can never be sure," the furniture dealer warns. "Next thing we know, a bomb will go off in the building."

The furniture dealer has a weighty voice in condominium matters because he owns not only the apartment on the fourth floor where he and his family live, but also the *attico,* or penthouse, which he rents out. Right now it is vacant, and the furniture dealer is looking for a foreign tenant, possibly an American with a lot of money. "Never again an Italian," he explains. "They only cause trouble. They don't pay the rent after the second month, and they won't leave. You have to sue them and are lucky to get them out in five years." The truth is that the furniture dealer wants to avoid the restraints of the new "fair rent" law.

Recent legislation has set rental ceilings for urban dwellings according to their location, size, and quality. Although the penthouse on the Aventine falls into the top category, its owner knows how to get much more by evading the law. To start with, he has put beds, tables, and a few other pieces from his storerooms—not the best ones—into the *attico,* because the "fair rent" law doesn't apply to furnished apartments. The last tenant was a Sicilian baron who knew all the tricks; over the years he himself had furnished the penthouse, which he used during his many visits to Rome. If he hadn't died under somewhat mysterious circumstances, the furniture dealer would have had a hard time getting him to give up the apartment. It won't be empty for long, because the headquarters of the Food and Agriculture Organization, with its hundreds of well-paid international officials, is nearby, not to mention all the Arab diplomats who are in the market for just such a place as the *attico* on the Aventine.

Other apartments around the city, especially if they are in central or otherwise desirable spots, are being rented out as offices rather than as dwellings. The "fair rent" law ignores offices, and any price goes. If in addition to a desk, a typewriter, and a filing cabinet, the tenant moves in a double bed, living-room furniture, and kitchen appliances and starts living in the place, maybe with a family, it's not the landlord's business. The contract covers office rent.

Apartment hunters who insist on a "fair rent" will have trouble finding a place, and if against all odds they do, they'd better bring their own tape measure. The yardstick kindly offered by the landlord to measure the space may be a little short—say, 95 centimeters instead of 100 to the meter—and the number of square meters to be rented, on which the "fair rent" is based, will be larger than it is in reality.

While there are few apartments for rent on any terms, thousands of empty ones are for sale. The city's two chief advertising vehicles, *Il Messaggero* and *Il Tempo,* run column after column of offers. Romans go heavily into debt to secure a place to live. If someone happens to have surplus cash, maybe after collecting severance pay, the most popular way of investing it is to rush into the real estate market.

Ownership of a unit in an apartment house has been a Roman way of life since antiquity, only lately adopted on a large scale by other Western countries. Most Roman families are parties to a condominium arrangement, or to more than one, either as tenants who have to refund condominial expenses to the landlord or as owners of their own or other apartments.

Such is human nature that condominium owners are far more often at odds than in agreement. In the endless condominial debates, apartment owners with little schooling and lowly jobs, or housewives who are famous for their pasta and cakes, often reveal unsuspected gifts for dialectics, legal quibbling, and tenacious defense of their own interests.

Thousands of condominium meetings all over the city every week fight over such issues as repainting. In the building on the Aventine there is a big battle every autumn about when to start heating; some want warm apartments as soon as possible, others would like to save money and wait until the weather turns really cold. One year Luisa reported at the last moment that the furnace had sprung a leak and needed to be repaired. The furniture dealer said Luisa's lazy husband might have checked out the heating system at the end of summer to see whether it worked all right. For some time he has been pressing for Luisa's dismissal. Now he suggests that one of the workers in his store might look after the automatic furnace from time to time and do other small jobs for the building.

One who was particularly stubborn in insisting that the *portiera* must stay was the retired general who lives with his daughter on the second floor. The daughter has a good job with a lawyer near the Palace of Justice and is away most of the day. The general, in his early eighties, is known to be in love with Luisa. Whenever she is in her little enclosure, which isn't too often, he soon joins her, to talk about what he has read in *Il Tempo* and seen on television. Luisa used to listen to him patiently, but since he failed to swing the condominial vote in her favor she is sullen with the general, too, causing him visible distress.

The general actually had cast two votes in favor of keeping Luisa on, one for himself and the other on behalf of a neighbor, the absentee owner of an apartment inhabited by two young women from Latin America who work at some embassy. They seem to be paying a good rental to their landlady, who has gone to live with relatives in Umbria and rarely comes to Rome now. The landlady has counted on Luisa to keep her informed about anything concerning her apartment. The two Latin Americans entertain a lot and sometimes allow friends to use the apartment during the day or stay over for a night. The other morning a young man, reportedly in the buff, was seen on the terrace.

Recently a plainclothes policeman took Luisa aside and asked her what kind of people the two foreign women were seeing. The two have often tipped the *portiera,* and Luisa told the policeman their guests were just nice young persons who were having a good time, nothing more. She also let one of the two woman tenants know in confidence that the police had made inquiries.

To any *portiera,* this episode is all in a day's work. Building superintendents have since time immemorial been police informers in Rome. The Fascist regime institutionalized the relationship; janitors needed a police license and were supposed to watch out for lawbreakers, troublemakers, and antifascists. Luisa is considered a valuable source for the police. At one time or another she has been in every apartment in her building and, in her visits to administer shots, in many others in the Aventine district. She knows a lot of neighborhood gossip and, having lived for so long in the same place, has seen many children grow up and has some idea what they are doing now.

"With someone like you on the street, we can be pretty sure there aren't any hidden terrorists around," the plainclothesman who quizzed her remarked. "It's a pity you too are going."

"Tell that to my employers," said Luisa, meanwhile thinking she must make one more trip to union headquarters in a day or two. The irony of her situation—that the union's gains for building superintendents have been the cause of her loss—escapes her.

COLLECTIBLES AND COMMUNISTS

Laura's small, plush apartment is not far from the Gallery of Modern Art just outside the Borghese Gardens. It looks like a hideaway branch of that institution. Paintings and drawings by de Chirico, Morandi, de Pisis, Guttuso, Rosai, Vespignani, and others—some alive, the others well remembered by her—cover the walls of her home.

Sometimes a work that Laura's guests have admired for years may disappear from her living room and be replaced with a modern print or a sketch by one of her many creative friends. Such changes occur when Laura gets a particularly good offer for a picture she owns, usually from a client whose apartment she is doing or redoing.

Laura isn't really a collector or an art dealer. She is a free-lance decorator who dabbles in the art trade and makes a lot of money. New business comes to her all the time through word of mouth. Most clients appear to trust her taste and to appreciate her efficiency. She says she has her own "cast" (she uses the English word while speaking in Italian): a team of plumbers, electricians, a stucco worker, painters, a paperhanger, cabinetmakers, and other craftsmen who are on call and are glad to do jobs for her because they know they will be paid well and at once.

Right now Laura and her cast are quite busy. "There seems to be plenty of cash around. Everybody is afraid of inflation, and people are withdrawing into private life and want beautiful homes. They also want second homes in the country or at the seaside," she tells me. "Some of my best customers are Communists. They have the money, they hanker for the refined life, and they have the second homes, too. You should see their villas. Is there any poor Communist in Italy?" She names a Communist painter who, she asserts, "lives like a prince. His butler serves tea with white gloves."

When I first met Laura several years ago she was very sympathetic toward the Communist Party, doubtless influenced by her left-wing friends—intellectuals and artists— and by her daughter, who was a student then and now has a theatrical job in Paris. Decorating the homes of well-to-do Communists has apparently changed Laura's views about the Party. Her clients of course aren't the rank-and-file Communists who sell the party organ, *l'Unità*, in the streets on Sunday or put up wall posters for electoral rallies. She does business with the fat cats whom the Communist Party apparatus has placed in lucrative posts in banks, economic agencies, the state broadcasting system, and other branches of the subgovernment. The number and influence of Communists in such key positions proves that their party has long become a pillar of the Roman establishment.

I know one of Laura's Communist clients. He is in his early seventies, has long been a member of the Communist Party's central committee, and is now co-chairman of a semigovernmental body with a large budget deficit that the taxpayers have to cover year after year. He is also a learned man, one of the best Latinists I know, and an art connoisseur. Recently he bought some nineteenth-century drawings and a fragment of an ancient Roman statue from Laura. He is sometimes a guest at the intimate dinner parties that Laura has given almost every week for quite some time. She always does the cooking herself; her risottos are justly famous. Meals at Laura's are serious sit-down affairs, not the messy buffet dinners that Romans dislike.

Years ago, when the Communist notable was still very active in his party's apparatus, he said over wine in Laura's place one night that he had been in the Soviet Union at least thirty times. "What uncouth people!" he remarked. "Getting drunk quickly is their ideal. They wouldn't sip this noble Chianti slowly, the way it deserves to be savored. They would empty the entire bottle in five minutes and yell for vodka. How distant they are from our civilization!"

Not all Italian "Eurocommunists" are so candid when they speak about their Soviet comrades, but Laura's guest sounded as if he were echoing a widespread state of mind among intellectuals in his party. He turned to me and said he didn't think much of culture in the United States either, although he had never been there.

Now, Laura tells me, she is about to help her friend redecorate his city apartment in an ancient palazzo near the Tiber; he and his wife have decided to move much of their furniture into a seaside cottage they have just bought. "I am building their new living room around some paintings of the great Roman seventeenth-century school that I found for them years ago," she told me. "I am getting them some delightful eighteenth-century furniture that friends of mine tracked down in Naples and had restored by an expert. That living room will be a gem." How much will it all cost? "It won't be cheap, but they can afford it." To better protect the Communist bigwig's apartment from burglars, one specialist in Laura's team will line the entrance door with steel plate, install new locks, and secure the windows.

At the same time, Laura is negotiating the sale of a small lot of modern paintings to a *monsignore* who has an inordinate interest in contemporary art.

How did Laura acquire her expertise and her connections in the art and antiques trade? It is a long story, and though I don't know all of it, I've glimpsed some phases of it over the years. Laura was married young to a southerner nearly twenty years older than she whose family owns hotels and other real estate. They soon separated—without much bitterness, it seems—and they agreed that Laura would bring up their only child, a daughter.

The girl had just started high school when Laura became the steady companion of one of Rome's leading painters. They never lived together, but Laura spent much of her time in her friend's split-level studio near the Spanish Square, and she gradually became his business manager as well as his companion. She dealt with the gallery that showed and sold his works, and took care of his bills and taxes.

For years Laura and the painter were a well-known couple in Rome's art crowd. They met with other artists, writers, and critics for aperitifs outdoors at the Caffè Canova or the Caffè Rosati in the Piazza del Popolo before lunch. They attended vernissages, patronized the fashionable trattorias, and were to be seen in the front rows at theater premieres. Money was no problem. Laura got enough support money from her husband to send her daughter to an expensive convent school where the girl became an atheist and a radical, and the painter was flooded with commissions by rich people, many from northern Italy, who were eager to pull out their checkbooks and pay advances just to get on his waiting list.

Laura's affair with her painter was at its height in the mid-1960s, when Rome seemed well on its way to becoming one of the most important world centers of modern art. New galleries sprang up almost every week. Since the last century, artists have congregated in the district between the Spanish Square and the Piazza del Popolo. Many of them found studios in the buildings on the narrow, romantic Via Margutta, whose backyards look out on the slopes of the Pincio Hill where a few private gardens of a bucolic past have survived to this day. Rome's oldest art galleries are in this neighborhood, especially in the Via del Babuino, which runs parallel to the Via Margutta. In the years when Laura and the painter walked from the Spanish Square through the Via del Babuino to the Piazza del Popolo for their aperitifs almost every day, less affluent artists were already being crowded out of that section of the city. Business executives from Milan and industrialists from Turin who visited Rome regularly and wanted a pied-à-terre in an arty setting rented what had been artists' studios in the Via Margutta.

Adriano Olivetti, the late typewriter king from Ivrea who championed industrial design and community planning, had a penthouse in the Via del Babuino. Rents for apartments, studios, and lofts in the neighborhood became prohibitive for artists who were not, or not yet, big-timers. Young painters and sculptors looked for working space in other parts of the city, preferably downtown, and the art dealers followed them, opening galleries around the Piazza Navona and elsewhere. Business was thriving. Storeowners, dentists, middle-class Romans who had come into money started buying canvases by little-known painters whose work they liked or had been talked into liking, in the hope that the painter would one day become famous and their purchase would then be worth many times the original price. Or, if one had more money, one might pick up a de Chirico of the first, surrealist, manner; there always seemed to be a few in the market.

Never mind that the old master himself, who was still alive then, might furiously denounce the painting as a fake if he was asked to authenticate it. Better not make such a request. Giorgio de Chirico still walked from his home in the Spanish Square to the nearby Caffè Greco in the Via Condotti at noon every day and sat down at a marble-topped table, seemingly not noticing that tourists were pointing him out to each other. Admirers and acquaintances greeted the famous artist with the imperious features, and he unsmilingly acknowledged the homage. Behind his back the connoisseurs whispered that the maestro might, after all, have a hand himself in the mysterious multiplication of de Chiricos.

It was a heady time then to be an artist in Rome, especially a well-established artist, like Laura's friend. Talented painters from abroad who had just won a scholarship at the American Academy on the Janiculum Hill or at some other foreign institution in the city came to pay respects and ask for advice. Young artists from the Italian provinces who had just moved to Rome also turned up to ask Laura if she knew of a cheap loft, or maybe a garage, in some old building in Trastevere. A few of them made it in the capital, and Laura is still in touch with them.

Maybe Laura got a bit carried away in her patronage of newcomers. She says her painter, who had always been rather possessive and jealous, now started making dreadful scenes, torturing her with unfounded accusations that she was unfaithful. It was a miserable time for her, Laura recalls, because her former husband was just then having trouble with the latest in a series of young mistresses, and almost daily used to call up his estranged wife, often after midnight, to pour out his anguish about his passion being repaid with betrayal. "I comforted him as best I could," Laura says, "but for months he kept me on the phone literally for hours almost every night." Laura's husband eventually was abandoned by his mistress, and she herself broke up with her painter. Laura started dabbling in interior decorating both because she needed more money and because she felt she had to do something on her own. Her daughter had gone to Paris to complete her studies, and remained there when she was taken on by a theater.

Laura, now in her early fifties and quite successful in her chosen line of business (and, I suspect, in dodging income taxes), is also a person to consult if one considers buying a painting, a sculpture, or an antique and wants advice on whether the asking price is reasonable. The market has changed since the years when Laura and her painter were a fixture in the arty cafés and trattorias. As inflation accelerates, there are still many moneyed people who want to invest in such collectibles as modern paintings, but they are now distrustful of unknown artists. "In the 1960s anything seemed to go," Laura explains. "A young painter or sculptor had a market because there was always some buyer willing to gamble on a possible genius." Actually, though, there weren't any future Picassos in Rome at that time, and nobody seems to have made a real killing in the art market. The works of contemporary artists who were then already generally recognized are still in demand, but many others who were promising unknowns are still obscure, and their work shows up only in the tourist trade and the periodic Via Margutta outdoor art fair.

Collectors and investors increasingly turn to paintings and drawings from the seventeenth through the nineteenth centuries. Few can afford what little genuine Renaissance art is in the market. However, a brisk faking industry is turning out old masters, skillfully treating and overpainting musty, long unnoticed canvases that have been found in the corners of a church or a palazzo.

Tied in with the trade in art fakes is trafficking in relics from antiquity, authentic or not. Chunks of statuary, coins, vases, and other artifacts find their way to Rome from the Etruscan cemeteries north of the city, where hundreds of professional tomb robbers are at work, or from archaeological diggings in Sicily and elsewhere. My friend Italo, an officer in a special Carabinieri task force that seeks to protect the nation's cultural patrimony, has just arrested a mafioso who attempted to smuggle into Switzerland a bronze head of the sea-god Poseidon, valued at $2 million. The fragment belonged to a life-size Greek statue and had been stolen much earlier from the museum near the celebrated Doric temples of Paestum, south of Salerno.

One of the most important centers for marketing hot works of art and archaeological treasures is Zurich. When such items have been stolen or looted in Italy, they usually pass clandestinely through Rome on their way to Switzerland. Professional smugglers and officials of some embassies who are able to use the diplomatic pouch for shady private purposes sometimes pick up hot objects directly in the Italian capital and spirit them abroad, saving the stiff commissions that the Zurich middlemen charge.

I asked an official who is engaged in the recovery of looted art where the trafficking in Rome was going on. "Watch some of the many art galleries and antiques stores," he said.

"Not the reputable ones, which are well known in the trade and among collectors, but certain other ones. You may not see any clients enter these places for days. How can such businesses survive? And yet they do."

Such stores, the official explained, were only a front for illegal dealing in hot stuff, maybe a Caravaggio that had been stolen from a church, a dubious Tintoretto with an authentication by a complaisant expert, or a piece of Etruscan pottery that might have been dug up by a tomb robber in the necropolis of Cerveteri or fabricated by a forger in Volterra. The items weren't on display in the shop, of course, they were being kept in some secret storeroom, possibly in a private apartment. "If a crooked dealer sells just one valuable piece every month, he is doing fine," the art sleuth told me.

Laura is not mixed up in any such skulduggery, but some of her contacts maintain lines of communication with the art and antiques underground. The intertwining of disparate social strands is indeed typical for Rome, where everybody knows someone who knows a cardinal or a rich heiress, a mafioso or a Communist senator, a diplomat or a thief.

THE NEWSSTAND

The newsstand in the Piazza San Silvestro is one hundred years old, a reason for celebrating. Veteran journalists crowd around Pietro Censi, the manager—who has long been a neighborhood character—drinking champagne out of vermouth glasses and paper cups. Pietro, a short, barrel-chested man and a Lazio enthusiast since his boyhood, has wet eyes and mumbles, "If only Mama and Papa were here today." They are long dead; I knew them both.

Pietro's business isn't just another newsstand. The oldest customers call it Orsi's, the name of his maternal grandfather, an unforgotten original. He permitted his many journalist friends to read all the newspapers without buying them.

At that time, reporters for newspapers in Italy's provincial cities, and foreign correspondents, wrote their dispatches by hand on telegraph forms and turned them in at the general post office on the north side of the square. The post and telegraph services are still housed in the same old building, a former convent that once belonged to the adjoining Church of St. Sylvester. It is now quite inadequate as a communications center.

Many Romans who live in outlying districts still insist on mailing letters at the Piazza San Silvestro or sending telegrams from there in the mistaken belief that service will be faster than from the branch post offices in their own neighborhoods. If nothing else, it's a pretext for going downtown, mingling with the crowds, showing off one's new dress or hairdo, window-shopping, dropping in at a fancy espresso bar, and maybe meeting somebody one hasn't seen for weeks.

Journalists have long given up on the general post office and now file their reports by telex and phone from other places. However, they still gravitate toward the Piazza San Silvestro, and many buy the newspapers and magazines they need at Pietro's stall. In addition to Rome's eighteen dailies, almost all of the more than fifty out-of-town papers, scores of periodicals, and many foreign publications can be had there.

The Piazza San Silvestro, close to the Chamber of Deputies and the prime minister's office in the Palazzo Chigi, has remained the outdoor press center of the Italian capital. Most of the big, important provincial newspapers, like *Corrière della Sera* of Milan and *La Stampa* of Turin, have their Rome bureaus nearby. The Roman Press Association's offices are only two blocks away, and the Foreign Press Association headquarters is on the east side of the square.

Several lines of the city's bus system start in the Piazza San Silvestro. When the buses stop running after midnight, the square doesn't go to sleep. Night owls can always find a cab in the piazza. Until recently, they could also drop in at the all-night pharmacy. The Farmacia Garinei, as the place is called, served for generations of Romans as a late-hour refuge that had, like Pietro's newsstand, its own set of regulars. The post-midnight people used to discuss their health complaints or the latest Roman scandal with the imperturbable pharmacist on night duty, swallow pills and chase them with water from the wall fountain, sit down to rest, watch a hurried client ask for a package of prophylactics or a suspected junkie try unsuccessfully to get a drug that is on the restricted list, and make "sorry-if-I-woke-you-up" calls from the pay phone. Then, "Dr. Gualtiero," the night man, retired; no replacement for him was found, and the old pharmacy started closing at eight P.M. "Alas, Rome at night isn't what it used to be," said the owner, Pietro Garinei.

Once, journalists, writers and artists had a haven in the famous "third room" of the old Café Aragno a few steps from the Piazza San Silvestro. Guests drank their *cappuccino,* read newspapers they had bought at Orsi's, wrote articles or notes for a book, and exchanged news and rumors. One prominent critic and writer habitually brooded at a corner table, wearing a thick, shabby coat in winter and summer. During Mussolini's dictatorship the third room was notoriously saturated with informers of the Fascist secret police, the OVRA, who pretended to be absorbed with the sports pages while eavesdropping on the conversation at neighboring tables.

The third room has since been closed and taken over by a furniture store and a haberdasher's. The Café Aragno itself, after various transformations, has resumed its old name, but is now a snack bar without much conversation and, presumably, without police spies. But the Piazza San Silvestro is still a good place for picking up information. Invariably one runs into somebody there who is eager to pass on the latest succulent gossip. A few times I have first learned of important news while browsing at Pietro's stand. The Italian journalists I meet there by chance are immensely more informative—and also more amusing—in their conversation than they are in their published prose.

Ask a Roman reporter or writer about the latest developments on the domestic scene and he will come up with piquant detail, racy anecdote, and shrewd assessment. But don't read what he writes about the same matter. Following is the faithful translation of the first few paragraphs of a political story taken at random from *Il Messaggero,* which has the largest circulation of all Roman dailies:

> In the DC the polemics between the majority and the Zaccagnini area have become harsher. After the criticisms by Granelli and Cabras, Baldassarre Armato, an exponent of the left who is very close to Bodrato, intervened yesterday.

155

According to Armato, the hard line adopted in the Chamber by the PCI, which resulted in the government finding itself in the minority regarding the 1978 account, is the reply to the speeches by Piccoli and Donat Cattin in Brescia and to the "line of confrontation demanded by the preamble-ists" who won the last congress.

"This line," he added, "serves only to degrade the political dialogue. The very problem of the morality of the parties and of the leading class is being pushed upon a watershed in a war of detergents aimed at showing who is wearing the dirtier shirt." Etc., etc.

The abbreviations, the insiders' shorthand, the names of prominent and obscure politicians without further identification, the mixed metaphors, the confusing quotes, and the clumsy phrasing all appear in what is supposed to be a popular newspaper. The sample is fairly typical of the ponderous and cryptic way in which much of the Italian daily press is written. Maybe a few thousand Romans who closely follow politics, if they aren't active in it, will understand what it is all about, but to most readers of *Il Messaggero* the account is like a text in Romanian or a secret code—it sounds like Italian but makes no sense to them.

A translation is in order. "DC" means the Christian Democratic Party. The "Zaccagnini area" is current political jargon for a faction of Christian Democrats allied around the party's former secretary, Benigno Zaccagnini, who advocate some kind of collaboration with the Italian Communist Party ("PCI"). "Exponent of the left" is a leading Christian Democrat belonging to one of various left-of-center groupings in his quarrelsome party. The "1978 account" is the government's long-overdue official statement on the national revenue and expenditures during that year, which has to be approved, but wasn't, by the Chamber of Deputies. The "preamble-ists who won the last congress" are an alliance of

Christian Democratic factions that at their party's last national convention gained a slim majority on the basis of a motion whose introductory statement, or preamble, ruled out any participation of Communists in the government. "War of detergents" and the following phrase, taken from the parlance of advertising copy, refer to the perennial debate as to which of Italy's many parties is more corrupt than the others.

A glossary like the foregoing ought to accompany most reports on political, economic, and cultural topics in Italian dailies. Small wonder that almost everybody who picks up a newspaper skips the gibberish and looks for the news on crime and scandals, or for the sports section or even the advertisements, which at least have the advantage of being understandable.

The writing in much of the Italian press explains to a large extent why in a country with a population of 57 million the more than seventy dailies have a combined circulation of only 5 million; fewer than one out of every ten Italians ever buys a newspaper. Another reason is the prevalence of the spoken over the printed word in a southern culture with an extensive outdoor life. Romans in particular aren't known as avid readers. Local educators speak about a "return illiteracy" of persons who had learned to read in school but later in life got out of practice, never taking a book, and rarely a newspaper or magazine, in hand. Ride in a Roman bus and watch how many adults look at the drawings or photos in some comic book; one wonders if they take the trouble to read the brief phrases in the balloons of the picture frames. It is estimated that one out of every five Italians regularly turns to the comic books.

Although the newspapers are ignored by many Romans and appear to be losing further ground to the electronic media, journalists are privileged and envied. They are part of the establishment, even if they belong to a news organization or political group that happens to oppose the government. Members of the press make good salaries, enjoy lavish fringe benefits, are granted a 70 percent reduction when they travel on the state railroads and a 30 percent cut on tickets for domestic flights, are favored by the telephone company, hobnob with politicians, receive Christmas payola from the public relations departments of large corporations and from lobbyists, and easily obtain free passes to cinemas.

It is therefore hardly surprising that countless young people in the provinces dream of becoming journalists in the capital. It's not all that easy. To be accepted as a member of the national press federation and obtain the coveted press card, a candidate must first find a trainee's job in a newspaper or other news organization, and after some time pass an exam on political, economic, and cultural subjects. Well-known and long-established writers who wanted the status of professional journalists have taken the written and oral tests. For every job opening there are hundreds of applicants. It's much harder to find a plumber or a cook in Rome than a journalist. In addition to the reporters, writers, and editors of the local and out-of-town dailies, the news agencies, and the many magazines, several hundred more are on the staffs of the oversized rival news departments of RAI, the state radio and television network. The Roman press community is further swelled by the public relations personnel of the ministries, other government agencies and semigovernmental bodies, business corporations, and pressure groups.

The privileges of the press in Italy have roots in the Fascist system. Mussolini always regarded himself as a journalist. He was editor-in-chief of the Socialist Party organ, *Avanti!*, before he started the Fascist movement and founded his own newspaper, *Il Popolo d'Italia.* After he seized power, he continued writing occasional articles for it, and until the end he kept in touch almost daily with its editorial offices in Milan. As government chief, even during the war years when he should have had more urgent things to do, Mussolini spent a considerable amount of time every day scanning Italian and foreign newspapers. He had accumulated knowledge in many disparate fields in the broad, general, and often shallow way of journalists, and gave the impression to his aides that the hours at his desk with piles of fresh dailies to read, annotate, and clip were among his happiest. He should have remained a newsman.

Under the Fascist regime the Italian press was heavily censored and rang with chauvinistic rhetoric. However, Mussolini saw to it that journalists were well paid and enjoyed working conditions considered among the best anywhere. The privileges of Italian press personnel survived Mussolini and have been strengthened in periodic labor-management contracts since World War II. A second-string parliamentary reporter who picks up his newspapers at Pietro's stand in the Piazza San Silvestro earns more than an army general. He told me he stands to collect severance pay running to more than $100,000 if he gives up his job or goes into retirement or if his newspaper happens to close. As long as his present employers stay in business he practically can't be fired, because in addition to the severance pay, the management would have to count on union trouble and endless lawsuits. Some tottering newspapers are said to continue publishing only because they can't afford to fold and pay off their staffs.

Not surprisingly, almost all Italian dailies are losing money and would have to close down if they weren't being subsidized by the government, by political parties and factions, by state-controlled industries, by big business, or by a combination of such benefactors. Some of the largess is reserved for the press that supports the government or at least isn't too hostile. Other favors are showered on the entire newspaper industry indiscriminately. For instance, newsprint quotas are apportioned to all dailies at a cost to them below the free-market price; the government—meaning the taxpayer—makes up the difference. Hidden subsidies are channeled to favored newspapers or magazines through publicity agencies, directly or indirectly controlled by the government, guaranteeing annual minimum advertising revenue. Special legislation has recently earmarked public funds for easy credit to ailing newspapers that should help them pay off the high-interest bank debts they have run up.

The plethoric press corps in Rome nevertheless often does bite the hand that feeds it, although perhaps not hard enough. But to learn what the journalists really know and think about the powerful personages on the Roman scene, there's nothing like keeping your ears open in the Piazza San Silvestro.

RAI'S ROME

When Corrado walks anywhere in Rome, people nudge each other and turn around, motorists stick their heads out of their cars to shout "Ciao, Corrado!" and youngsters rush up to beg for his autograph on the back of a comic book or whatever else comes to hand. He is often on magazine covers, and his portrait is on the box of a parlor game he has endorsed. Few Romans remember his family name, Mantoni; his first name is enough.

For years, Corrado has hosted the show on state television with the highest ratings. He was master of ceremonies of a six-hour marathon every Sunday afternoon, with an attractive young woman as a sidekick, guest appearances by other beauties and by people in the news, a quiz—and, throughout the show, when the biannual soccer championship was in progress, live or recorded shots from games in stadiums around the nation. The format simply couldn't fail; Corrado was possibly the most popular figure in all Italy.

Then, disaster. The entertainer was driving back to Rome in the early morning hours after a late-evening appearance as the emcee at a non-television affair in Civitavecchia, the seaport city north of Rome, when his car went out of control and crashed into a guardrail. Corrado was badly injured; his latest TV sidekick, Dora Moroni, who had been with him on the stage in Civitavecchia, was in a coma.

It took weeks before Corrado was out of the hospital and well enough to be on the tube again. Wearing a harness under his suit for support, he sat in front of the cameras hosting his old Sunday afternoon show. Then he was re-placed, but the new emcee didn't have his success. Dora Moroni was also out of the hospital, but she couldn't speak yet. Slowly, slowly, she learned to say her first few words again.

Through lawyers, retained on her behalf by her family, Dora threatened to sue Corrado for huge damages on the ground that he had been at the wheel when his auto, for no discernible reason, swerved off the Civitavecchia-Rome motor road. Dora claimed an amount to cover medical and hospital bills, the cost of rehabilitation, and additional money to make up for the loss of what the lawyers asserted would have been a promising show business career. In out-of-court negotiations the parties reached a settlement that obliged Corrado to pay Dora hundreds of millions of lire.

This wasn't quite as easy for him as it might have been, because for several months Corrado had no TV show of his own. But he did appear regularly every evening on the main channel of the state network at the height of prime time, just before the eight P.M. news: he spoke a thirty-second message in praise of a detergent. The advertising spot went a long way toward straightening out his finances. And later, RAI decided it couldn't really do without him, and put him back on prime time with a lavish new show.

Corrado is only one of many Roman television celebrities who, while unknown abroad, fascinate Italians and at the same time help tighten the capital's hold on the popular culture of the entire nation. Billions of lire whirl around Corrado and the other celebrities that RAI has created. Their network pay, though generous, is only a small part of their incomes. Advertising work, endorsement of products, and, above all, personal appearances up and down the country earn them a great deal of extra money. Organizers of fashion shows and beauty contests, chamber of commerce boosters, winegrowers' cooperatives, business promoters from northern manufacturing centers to Mafia strongholds in Sicily—all are willing to pay hefty fees to get Corrado to show up in the flesh and say a few nice words about the products of Varese or Agrigento, hand out trophies, and laud the civic spirit of his hosts. Corrado and Dora were driving back to Rome from just such an appearance in Civitavecchia the night of the accident.

Even the dozen young women who do nothing more than take turns announcing RAI's programs three times a day enjoy nationwide fame, each with her own carefully nurtured persona, fan mail, agent, and commercial sidelines. Their private lives and romantic entanglements, true or invented, are grist for the gossip weeklies, and when they aren't scheduled to appear on their network they crisscross the country by air, railroad, and car to keep all their commitments. Fashion houses and jewelers press their creations on the announcers, begging them to wear this blouse or that necklace in front of the TV camera. No need to identify the products; thousands of women are sure to look for them in shop windows and buy them.

Much talent and substantial advertising revenues have lately been lured from RAI to private TV stations. One of these pulled off a coup when it signed up Mike Bongiorno, an Italian-American who for many years has been enormously popular as the leading quizmaster of the state network. He still is one of the best-known figures in the country, and is instantly recognized by many Italians who don't know, or care, who the current prime minister is.

Although RAI has lately been besieged by the enterprising "free" broadcasters, the state network has remained a power center that manipulates Italian public opinion, particularly through its news programs, mirroring the views of the dominant political factions. RAI, with a bloated staff of no fewer than fourteen thousand, is also an important Roman employer, a patron of artists and entertainers, still the nation's most effective advertising medium, a stage for political power plays and intrigue, a steady source of gossip, and a national mythmaker.

Through RAI, Rome today looms larger in the thoughts,

163

imagination, and dreams of Italians throughout the country than it did at any time since it became the capital in 1870. The city is still not generally loved by a nation that was unified only in the second half of the last century. Millions of Italians have greater affection for, say, Venice or Naples than for Rome. Milanese, Florentines, Sicilians, and natives of many other regions look down on the Romans.

Yet Italians at large depend more than ever today on Rome as their model for life-styles, idiom, and tastes, whether they know it or not, simply because they watch so much television. Almost all RAI programs that aren't imported, like American films and shows, are produced in the capital and reflect its way of doing and seeing things. The national Parliament, the government buildings, the Vatican, Roman monuments and street scenes—all are familiar sights to the provincial audiences. Roman vernacular and Roman attitudes—the characteristic lassitude, the bonhomie, the mockery of any *fanatico,* the flashes of cynicism and coarseness—pervade the TV series, the talk shows, and even the advertising spots. Unwittingly, millions throughout the country imitate how Corrado and the other Roman video idols dress, speak, and act.

Above all, RAI powerfully influences the colloquial language. Roman idiom and dialect have penetrated into parts of the country that until recently stubbornly clung to their own speech patterns. In homogenizing—and vulgarizing—the Italian language, RAI is continuing and reinforcing a process that began with the films Cinecittà turned out for home consumption starting in the late 1930s.

The Italian language has many dialects, some quite disparate. Venetians and Sicilians, for instance, don't understand each other when they speak in their own regional idioms. Standard Italian, as taught in school and to some extent spoken by educated persons, is based on the vocabulary and grammar (though not necessarily on the pronunciation) of Tuscany. However, for a long time Roman sounds and words have been encroaching on pure Florentine, whence the hackneyed definition of good Italian as *"lingua toscana in bocca romana"* (Tuscan language in a Roman's mouth).

Italian, as everybody knows, is one of the gentlest and most melodious languages on earth. In a "Roman's mouth" it becomes a coarse syrup. Italians elsewhere in the country have never liked the capital's lazy vernacular with its lack of precision and its many vulgarisms, but now they all are absorbing more and more of it.

Under the impact of the Rome-oriented electronic media even the pronunciation of standard Italian seems to be changing. For instance, an increasing number of Italians appear unable now to say the few words in their language that end with a consonant, or similar foreign terms and names, without blurring them the way the Romans have always done. Thus *sud* (south) becomes "soodde," *sport* is pronounced "sportah," and the name of a former head of state, Saragat, inevitably turns into "Saragatte." San Remo and Marilyn Monroe are generally rendered as "Sarremo" and "Marilimorro."

Through films, radio, and television, Roman popular speech has also introduced into colloquial Italian a few untranslatable voice signals that often go with gestures. One is *"uoh!"*—to seek someone's attention or register a protest. Then there is *"boh!"*—a belching sound that means "I don't know, and I couldn't care less." Another acoustic shorthand symbol is a rising, unpleasantly truncated *"eh!"* that comes at the end of an explanation or contention, conveying the thought "you don't see my point, you dope, do you?"

The Roman dialect is far less elegant than the Tuscan. Rome's greatest vernacular poet, Giuseppe Gioacchino Belli, who served as a papal lay official during the first half of the nineteenth century, was often gross in his satirical sonnets that savaged the Vatican administration. There is much historical evidence that Romans of all social classes have always loved to pepper relaxed speech with vulgar words and phrases.

As for modern Italian, some ultimate restraints began to

yield around 1970, and obscenities that until then had been taboo for the mass media found their way into broadcasts and newspapers. Of course, this has also happened to other languages lately, and the Italian trend may have been reinforced through the dubbed dialogues of imported films and translations of foreign pop music lyrics.

When the Eternal City's favorite all-purpose expletive, *stronzo* (turd) was first heard on RAI, circa 1978, it was, because of the existence of the state broadcasting system, made acceptable for use by the entire country. A Roman cultural revolution.

PORNOVISION

The two small children in the next room had at last fallen asleep, and Pino's wife was tired and had dozed off. But Pino, at her side, was wide awake. Propped up on two cushions, he was working the gadget that electronically switches channels on the color television in a corner of their bedroom. The sound was turned off—who needs it? Pino, in his early thirties and already head of the computer department in a big bank, was watching the late-late porn shows and was seeking out the hardest of the hard-core films.

In the office next morning, before he heard about equipment glitches and complaints by bank customers, Pino exchanged comments on the programs of the night before with a bleary-eyed colleague, also a porn addict. "Electronic channel-switching is the biggest erotic breakthrough of the last several years" is an aphorism that the colleague kept repeating. A woman secretary giggled. She too had been glued to the blue tube until the small hours. Thousands of Romans are, night after night. They watch *Midnight Playboy,* striptease shows in which housewives and other amateur talent take it all off, and raunchy movies. The late-late sex wave in Rome's chaotic "free" television may soon be past its peak, even peter out, so let's enjoy it while it lasts.

Right now, television antennas in the city are being bombarded with signals from forty local stations in addition to those from the three channels of the state-controlled network. The private stations come and go, offering vintage movies, propaganda for political parties, situation comedy series bought in the United States, interminable talk shows, and, at night, nudity. Some stations are on the air only a few days and then disappear forever; others are packed with publicity spots, while new ones join in the fight for audiences and sponsors.

It is also a struggle for geographical vantage points from which to beam the programs to the capital. The most coveted place is the 3,113-foot-high Monte Cavo, the loftiest peak in the vicinity of Rome. The old Passionist convent on top of the mountain—now transformed into a hotel and restaurant—is surrounded by a forest of tall masts, the transmitting and booster gear of twenty television stations.

The armed forces want the masts removed and the hotel-restaurant closed. The authorities contend that the private television broadcasts interfere with the signals of the military air traffic control in the Rome region. Monte Cavo is indeed only a few miles distant from Rome's second airport, Ciampino. Although Fiumicino, close to the sea, is bigger and busier, Ciampino is important because not only does it handle some domestic flights and charter traffic, but it is also an air force base, often used by United States military aircraft.

Official explanations of any measure that is taken or proposed always meet in Rome with general disbelief. Romans are notoriously affected by *dietrismo,* or "behind-ism," a tendency to speculate forever as to what is behind some event or development. The Radical Party, for one, alleges that the military flight control argument is being used as a flimsy stratagem to black out the broadcasts from Monte Cavo in which it daily attacks the government.

Other insistent rumors that find their way into the newspapers name more ominous reasons for the armed forces campaign against the television masts on Monte Cavo: the whole mountain is larded with silos and launchers for tactical missiles, possibly with nuclear warheads; it is a secret base of the North Atlantic Treaty Organization; it hides in its entrails a three-story concrete bunker meant to serve as a refuge for the government and key personnel in case of emergency.

In the event of a military attack on Italy, the press speculates, the prime minister and his cabinet, the armed forces leadership, and other top officials would abandon their offices in Rome and repair to the command post inside Monte Cavo. It's a good story, but to people who live in Rocca di Papa, at the foot of Monte Cavo, it sounds unlikely. When was the huge underground refuge built, and who did the contracting job? One would, after all, have seen a few of the building workers in the local taverns now and then, and one would have noticed trucks with construction materials and maybe also with missiles. The Defense Ministry denies all the talk about secret installations on or inside Monte Cavo, and reluctantly permits the private television stations to leave their equipment on top of the mountain for the time being. However, the military authorities make clear that sooner or later they want full control of the peak. Maybe they would like to install a mess hall and quarters for air force personnel in the old convent.

The dispute over Monte Cavo stirs nostalgic memories among many longtime residents of Rome. For decades, couples with time on their hands and adventure on their minds would drive out to Rocca di Papa and, by way of a private road, up the mountain. Even on the hottest summer day it is agreeably cool up there, with many evenings outright chilly. After lunch on the terrace one could ask for a place to rest and would be shown into one of the frugally appointed guest rooms, once the cells of the Passionist friars. For dinner one could have a table in what was once the convent chapel, and one could stay overnight. The Passionist convent was built in 1783 by Cardinal York, the brother of Bonnie Prince Charlie, the Young Pretender, and himself a claimant to the English throne, who eventually became archbishop of the nearby see of Frascati. He couldn't have foreseen that one day there wouldn't be any Passionist friars on the mountain and that their cells would be taken over by passionate couples.

More than two thousand years before the friars chanted

matins and vespers on the top of Monte Cavo, a famous shrine to Jupiter rose there. Its exact site hasn't been determined so far, but proof of its existence in antiquity is a well-preserved Roman road leading from the foot of the mountain to the peak. The ancient "sacred" or "triumphal" road, paved with large basalt stones, is much steeper than the new motor road that reaches the mountaintop in serpentines.

During a Sunday outing many years ago I climbed the Roman route with a friend. We were walking briskly in the shade of tall chestnut trees. About halfway up we overtook a couple, the man much older than the woman, who had slowed down and appeared to be having a lovers' tiff. They didn't know us, but my companion and I immediately recognized the man. He was Palmiro Togliatti, then the chief of the Italian Communist Party. A few years earlier he had returned to Rome after long exile in the Soviet Union and a period in Spain as Stalin's representative to the Republican camp in the civil war. The young woman, we realized later, was Nilde Iotti, who was eventually to be Togliatti's common-law second wife and, long after his death, speaker of the Chamber of Deputies.

At the time of the scene on the slope of Monte Cavo, Togliatti was still married to Rita Montagnana, a former seamstress and old Communist militant who had shared the bleak Moscow years with him. But they were already estranged, and it was known that the secretary-general of the strongest Communist Party in the West, then in his late fifties, was seeing much of Nilde Iotti. She was twenty-six years younger than he, a graduate of Milan Catholic University, a former high school teacher, and a Communist member of Parliament.

Many puritanical old-guard Communists resented the romance of their leader with a young newcomer to the Party, particularly since his wife was a much-admired comrade. Divorce didn't exist in Italy at that time, but Togliatti eventually started living with Miss Iotti, and they later adopted a girl whose father had died in a riot, and brought her up as their daughter.

On that Sunday, we didn't find out whether Togliatti and his young companion ever made it to the top of Monte Cavo. We did, however, and had fettuccine, Bologna style, recommended to us by the manager of the restaurant and hotel, a genial Bolognese named Grimaldi. There was no television equipment around the former convent then.

Revisiting the place the other day, I found that the sweeping panorama of Rome and the *campagna romana* all the way to the sea was still unobstructed. But there were no fettuccine; cables and machines with twinkling lights and nervous dials were crammed into the erstwhile guest rooms and friars' cells. Many of the old chestnut trees had been cut, and the military had already gained a foothold in the form of ungainly concrete structures erected near the former convent. But I didn't see anything to indicate the existence of a big underground bunker or missile silos.

Sooner or later the television equipment will doubtless have to move to some other hilltop in the Rome area. The number of free channels may by then have shrunk. The government is at present readying legislation that would cut down the number of television stations in the country from more than four hundred to about seventy.

Whatever the future of television, Pino and other Roman nighttime viewers are confident that at least some of the titillating shows will survive even when they no longer can be beamed to them from the Monte Cavo.

FLEA MARKET
PAPARAZZO

Most mornings Dino helps his father, who has a stand at the Porta Portese flea market, and every evening he sits near the telephone. One ring, and Dino answers. "La Spaak has just arrived with a new man," someone whispers. "You've got plenty of time, they have only ordered the first course, spaghetti *alla puttanesca.* It's the third table on your right as you come in."

The voice on the phone is that of a waiter in a basement restaurant that pushes spaghetti with black olives and spices (*alla puttanesca,* "whore style") as one of its specialties. Right now the place is favored by the movie and television crowd. Dino has an arrangement with the waiter and is going to slip him a 10,000-lire bill for the tip-off.

The target is Catherine Spaak, the film actress who is a niece of the late Belgian statesman Paul Henri Spaak. She has been around Rome for quite some time. Her first marriage, to Fabrizio Capucci, the brother of an internationally known dressmaker, broke up quickly, and a Rome court awarded custody of their daughter to Fabrizio. La Spaak's second marriage, to Johnny Dorelli, a comedian, is also on the rocks after a child. Whom is she dating now?

Dino hops on his powerful motorcycle and thunders off to the restaurant. His mother will mind the phone, and he will check with her from time to time to make sure he doesn't miss some other signal from his network of informants. At the restaurant, not far from the Via Veneto, Dino walks in matter-of-factly and at short range shoots an entire roll of film of La Spaak and her escort. Neither seems to mind; the couple even draws closer. The restaurant manager ignores the scene. The Belgian actress doesn't make trouble for photographers; at this stage of her career she seems to welcome the publicity.

It was a different story a few days earlier, when the high-living son of a rich businessman who finances cheap movies beat up Dino and smashed his camera. Dino says he is going to file a complaint to the police alleging assault and battery, and will sue the irascible playboy for damage to his equipment. The photographer admits that he had sneaked into the garage of the building where the businessman's son had spent a couple of hours with a film starlet, and had waited for them to leave.

The assailant, who is in his late thirties, tells Dino's lawyer on the phone: "Listen, I don't give a damn if your paparazzo client takes my picture with some girl. I've slept with three hundred women and everybody knows it. But he had no business being in the garage. I thought he was a gangster and was trying to kidnap me. What would you have done in such a situation?" There probably will be an arrangement and Dino won't sue.

Dino says, "I am not a paparazzo; I am a photojournalist." He carries credentials from a news agency that has long been out of business, and he markets his pictures himself. The shots of La Spaak and her new friend may be welcome to one of the illustrated weeklies that specialize in the affairs, weddings, adulteries, breakups, divorces, and true or invented adventures of people ranging from British royalty to mousy little entertainers who think they'll land a big film role because they go to bed with the son of a fly-by-night producer.

The local magazines, such as *Eva Express* or *Novella 2000*, are today the principal market for the output of Dino and his many competitors. The gossip weeklies sell well—far better than the daily newspapers. It's a rare coup when Dino is able to burst breathlessly into the Rome bureau of some international photo agency to sell a picture that will be transmitted by satellite to New York and published in dailies and periodicals all over the world. Most of the people shown in the photos that he and his rivals offer nowadays are just too little known abroad.

Gone are the exhilarating days when the paparazzi were cursing and fighting for space on the altar steps in a packed church near the Forum as Tyrone Power and Linda Christian were getting married; or when Elizabeth Taylor and Richard Burton were playing hide-and-seek with reporters on the Ancient Appian Way. Dino was in school then; he missed the big time.

> Paparazzo, n, pl -razzi (It): A news reporter or photographer who doggedly searches for a story that can be sensationalized.

The dictionary definition fails to mention that the new entry is derived from the Roman surname—sixteen Paparazzos are listed in the local phone directory—that Fellini gave the archetypal picture hound in *La Dolce Vita*. Since big films aren't made in Rome anymore, and since life in the city is no longer so sweet, the paparazzo subculture has markedly declined. Some of the paparazzi of the heady old days have gone respectable and now work for the public relations departments of big corporations or are in the high-fashion circuit. Others have emigrated and joined foreign news organizations. Roman cameramen who started at home as paparazzi have distinguished themselves in faraway places from the Middle East to Vietnam. But many of Dino's colleagues and competitors now are hungry enough to snap pictures of middle-class weddings on Sunday.

Dino himself is busy Sundays selling transistor radios, television sets, tape recorders, cassette decks, and Japanese cameras, new and used, at his father's stand. Sunday is the big day at the Porta Portese, when thousands of Romans and, lately, quite a few foreigners mill amid the stands near the old gateway to the river port. It is more than a flea market. You can buy new furniture and old books, an exhaust pipe and muffler of a 1938 Harley Davidson motorcycle, the latest pop cassettes, nineteenth-century Ethiopian coins, new United States Navy uniforms, cut-rate bundles of fresh asparagus or crates of grapes according to the season, an immense variety of the shoulder-strap bags that Roman men so love to carry, blue jeans stitched together in some suburban shack and labeled "Oclahoma," ceramic dragons and digital watches from Hong Kong, racing bikes, tools for hobbyists, women's and men's apparel, and roasted peanuts.

Porta Portese is where the *trovarobe* ("things finder")—the propman—of a movie troupe goes first when the director wants something that isn't in the studio storerooms, like a cup for seven egg yolks that will figure in an orgy scene, or a turn-of-the-century sewing machine for a period film.

Porta Portese rises on the right bank of the Tiber. Walk through the gateway and you are in the outdoor market, which follows the river downstream for half a mile in a narrow, teeming, open-air corridor. On the opposite bank the remains of what was the river port of ancient Rome have just come to light in new excavations. The ruined silos for grain and bins for other provisions are discernible. Behind is Monte Testaccio, the 115-foot mound of throwaway earthenware jars for wine and oil and other cargo debris heaped up there by the ancients. As the Tiber leaves the city past the outlets of the Cloaca Maxima, the main wastage conduit of ancient Rome, and of the modern sewers, it takes on a nasty color and a foul smell, lazily flowing southwest toward the Tyrrhenian Sea. The city's inadequate water treatment plant —its first and only—is farther downstream.

It is a tacky neighborhood around Porta Portese, but it surely is alive. Dino and his parents have just moved into a new, small apartment house that overlooks the market and the Tiber. It's noisy, the smell from the river is stronger on some days than on others, and the entire area is congested with trucks and cars that climb up on the sidewalks—where they exist.

But the family's new home is near their business, Dino can quickly reach any point in the city on his motorbike, and it's better than the place they had before. They had been living on the ground floor of one of the huge buildings that real estate speculators had crammed into the Magliana district farther downstream in brazen violation of the zoning laws. Dino and his parents were always afraid that if the Tiber rose above the safety level it would spill over its dams and flood their apartment, together with all the other lower floors of the jerry-built Magliana housing projects.

Dino's father came to the neighborhood toward the end of the last war with the Allied armies, and he stayed on when they moved northward. He had been a small farmer and part-time mechanic in a town of the Ciociaria, the hill country between Rome and Naples, and had found a job with an American military motor pool, repairing Jeeps. He must have "arranged" a new existence in the capital as a black marketeer. He doesn't like to talk about it now, but Dino says his father had a Jeep of his own and was trafficking in American K rations, cigarettes, military blankets, and other contraband. When the black market of the first postwar years dried up, he found himself stranded in the Porta Portese market.

Like many other old-timers at Porta Portese, Dino's father traded for years in automotive material. The big flea market still functions as a huge pool of spare parts for new and vintage cars and motorcycles that come from wreckers, receivers, and directly from thieves. If your car radio is stolen, you may find it a week or so later at the Porta Portese market and buy it back. Prudent Romans, of course, lift the radio out of its enclosure and take it with them when they park their autos.

Dino's father decided early that there was more money, and maybe less risk, in audiovisual equipment than in car parts of dubious origin. He linked up with importers of radios and photographic articles, and is today able to sell the material at prices that are substantially lower than those in regular shops. He has almost no overhead—no sales personnel, no decor, no publicity, no store rent, just the fee he must pay to the city for the few square feet of public soil his stand occupies.

Dino, now in his late twenties, became interested in photography as a teenager when he dropped out of high school and started working with his father. The dark-haired lad with the broad face and shrewd eyes was a success as a salesman. He picked up photo know-how from suppliers and customers, and personally tried out every type of camera he was selling. He shot innumerable pictures of soccer games, girl friends, and flea market scenes. Habitués of the spare-part stands sometimes called him after a car crash when photos for the insurance company were needed.

He was already known as "Dino the paparazzo" at Porta Portese when he met a professional who had arrangements with movie publicity agents, magazines, and picture agencies. One day the photographer came to the market to browse. Dino sold him a new small camera after showing the customer some of the pictures he himself had taken with it. The news photographer told Dino to drop in at his office whenever he had some other new piece of equipment. Dino did so a few weeks later, and eventually became his new friend's legman and assistant. He worked in that capacity, off and on, for a couple of years until the two had a quarrel, apparently over a woman, and Dino decided to operate on his own.

By then he had learned a few tricks, like reading the gossip columns for leads, keeping in touch with press agents and tipsters, and waiting outside nightclubs for hours until his quarry would emerge. He has sold quite a number of pictures.

Dino is still hoping for the big breakthrough. "My problem is, the competition is enormous, and few things happen in Rome that interest foreign clients," he says. "Even if I sell a good exclusive to an Italian magazine, I have to fight afterward to get paid. I've done everything except weddings; I just can't stand there and say 'smile' while the bride's mother tugs at the veil."

He doesn't have to do weddings because he can always fall back on his profits from the Porta Portese market. And unless the Rome of his childhood returns, in the long run selling cameras may be more profitable for Dino than using them.

DOLCE VITA, GOOD-BYE

Federico Fellini doesn't seem eager to talk about *La Dolce Vita.* The director, at times saturnine, at others voluble, hasn't much to say whenever he is asked, once again, what has happened to the indolently hedonistic Rome—with a dash of angst—that he depicted in the 1960 film. Where would he go now if he had to remake it? In 1960 there was a reason for *La Dolce Vita,* Fellini remarks, but he wouldn't do it now. Then, in a characteristic self-contradiction, he adds: "But I probably would. I always make the same film."

Years ago, Fellini observed that to him the real Via Veneto, the locale for key scenes of *La Dolce Vita,* was the set built for him in Studio No. 5 of Cinecittà. Since then, the Cinecittà film studios have fallen on hard times and may be razed to make room for more suburban housing developments. And the Via Veneto that other Romans consider the real one hasn't lived up to the international fame that *La Dolce Vita* brought it. The street that Fellini glamorized has become tawdry, lined with travel bureaus, airline offices, a hamburger eatery, stores selling overpriced shoes and apparel, a double procession of neon signs, and café terraces with South Seas decor. The boulevard is populated with tourists, cabdrivers, high-class streetwalkers, touts for nightclubs, news vendors, pimps, mafiosi, and plainclothes policemen. Romans stay away from it if they can, especially after dark.

Members of the city's intelligentsia, artists, journalists, the few politicians with intellectual pretensions, and smart, beautiful women no longer meet in the Via Veneto as they did when *La Dolce Vita* was shot.

Yet Fellini's version of the Via Veneto remains in people's minds. My profession has taken me to all continents, and wherever I mentioned that I was based in Rome, someone would wink and say, "Ah, la dolce vita!" If I let on I was working for the *New York Times,* nobody was moved to exclaim, "Ah, Manhattan!" or "Ah, Broadway!" No single film has done so much as *La Dolce Vita* for fixing the image of a city, even on the mental screens of persons who have seen neither the movie nor Rome.

Life has again been imitating art. Before Anita Ekberg stepped into the basin of the Trevi Fountain in the Fellini picture, I had never heard of anybody taking such a midnight footbath. Since then, I have often seen screeching or giggling woman tourists, egged on by their escorts, doing the Ekberg act after dinner, a Rome-by-night ritual. The police now permanently patrol the Piazza di Trevi, since the president of the republic has his private home there, and they no longer allow people to wade into the basin. But the fountain has remained one of Rome's main attractions, a must for every guided tour. All day long, innumerable visitors— Americans, Japanese, Germans—are lined up elbow to elbow, taking snapshots of the stone Neptune and the other marine statuary above the cascading waterworks. Pictures to show around back home. "Ah, la dolce vita!"

If anything has survived of Rome's sweet life, it isn't at the Fontana di Trevi, with its hordes of package-tour gawkers, its souvenir stands, and the empty soft-drink cans in its basin; nor will it be found in the Via Veneto.

Officially, the broad street that winds up from the Piazza Barberini, past the Industry Ministry and the United States embassy to the Villa Borghese gardens, is called Via Vittorio Veneto. The name recalls the city in the Alpine foothills where one of the last battles of World War I was fought and the forces of Austria-Hungary were decisively defeated. The boulevard doesn't seem to care for the military reminiscences it is supposed to evoke.

The Via Veneto of *La Dolce Vita* is the street's three-block stretch from the Riviera-style Hotel Excelsior to the Roman walls where 1,400 years earlier General Belisarius battled the besieging Goths. On the terraces of Doney's, Rosati's, or the Strega (only the first of the three cafés still exists) during the balmy summer evenings in the 1950s, filmmakers, actors, artists, press agents, journalists, writers, and cuties from the Italian provinces or from Sweden who were dreaming of a big part in a Cinecittà production would be on display. Anyone could sit down, order a drink, and rub elbows with authors, listen to leading critics as they dissected the latest film or play (one would read it word for word in next day's newspaper), or watch a scriptwriter sidle up to a rich movie producer who had just arrived from Milan.

Later at night, the managing editor of one or another of the Roman dailies, having put the first edition to bed, would turn up and pontificate about the day's news. Giuseppe Saragat, the well-read Social Democratic leader who was eventually to become president of Italy, would come up from the Chamber of Deputies and join in the conversation, which might go on until long after midnight. One enjoyed those relaxed alfresco discussions. One was still appreciating the new political and cultural freedom after the stifling rhetoric of the Fascist system and the wartime fears.

Inevitably, the Via Veneto cast had its chorus of hangers-on—dazzled provincials, social climbers, adventurers, bored aristocrats and rich people, party girls on the make, would-be movie stars from the boondocks, and the paparazzi, who were unaware at the time that such was to be their generic name.

This is the world that Fellini attempted to portray in his film. He arrived in the capital from his native Romagna region in the declining years of the Mussolini dictatorship and started out as a cartoonist for the satirical weekly

Marc'Aurelio before making it in Cinecittà. Italian critics have contended that Fellini's entire opus betrays a provincial's wonderment at the sophistication and vices of the big city, both glamorized and caricatured in grotesque cameos. Was there ever the sweet life in Rome portrayed in *La Dolce Vita*? And what has happened to whatever there was of the Rome of the 1950s?

Turn for an answer to Franco Ferrarotti, a sociologist and phrasemaker who can always be relied upon to come up instantly with quotable opinions on everything. On *La Dolce Vita,* and whether it has left a cultural heritage, he says, "That world is dead and has never been replaced—maybe because, despite its facade, it was no more than a small-town piazza." According to Ferrarotti, modern Rome has never had a genuine cultural life, "neither then nor now," because the city lacks the necessary institutions and structures.

As if to exemplify this state of cultural deprivation, the Rizzoli bookstore on the Via Veneto has just been closed. The Milan-based communications empire that owned it could no longer afford to operate it just for the sake of prestige, and sold the premises to a bank. The bookstore opposite the American embassy used to stay open late and attracted many browsers. Among other prominent people, the chief of the Communist Party, Enrico Berlinguer, a closet intellectual, could sometimes be seen there.

The transformation of the Rizzoli store into a bank not only makes the Via Veneto poorer, it is a loss for the entire city. There are enough banks but few good bookstores in Rome. The national library is often inaccessible—either because the staff is on strike or the defects plaguing the new building must be repaired. When the institution does function, too many students line up early in the day for too few seats to read up for their exams. The city's other libraries aren't up to date or are highly specialized and generally don't welcome random readers. But Rome notoriously reads little anyway, and for the lackadaisical talk that is a characteristic of the sweet life, any restaurant chair in which one can slouch will do.

There is still plenty of languid conversation, especially in the warm months. Back from a day of lolling on the sand and stealing glimpses of topless woman sunbathers at nearby Fregene beach, friends will sit around a café table in some piazza to wait for the *ponentino,* the beneficial western breeze that faithfully springs up every summer evening. They sip their aperitifs and discuss where to go for dinner. The men have their shirts wide open, showing golden chains, crosses, and medallions over their virile chests. The deeply tanned women wear no bras under their tricots. They are all likely to adjourn eventually to a trattoria with tables on the sidewalk in Trastevere, and much later to another piazza for ice cream or a last coffee.

However, Roman squares at night are no longer as much fun as they used to be. There are still the stray musicians who go around with tin plates after their first number, and the dirty gypsy girls who beg, carrying sleeping babies that one assumes they have borrowed from mothers in the tribe. But now there are also young barbarians on motorcycles improvising ear-splitting gymkhanas, and one must watch out for purse snatchers and robbers, while junkies prowl the sidelines. Entire neighborhoods that used to savor their own low-key *dolce vita* of sidewalk gossip, a little flirting, and much lassitude over half a liter of Frascati or lemon ices now seem to be under a curfew. After dark, most residents stay at home, probably watching television, or sit on their terraces. Only the centurions of the extreme neofascist and leftist legions roam the streets to raid or bomb each other's hangouts, paint savage threats on the house walls—"Fascists, the Trionfale section will be your Vietnam!"—and bash in the windshields of a few parked cars.

Throughout the city, much of what has remained of the sweet life has retreated indoors, into apartments in winter and onto terraces in the warm months. Uncle Annibale's place near Marino is noteworthy as a secluded setting for political and business maneuvers, but Rome boasts thousands of other hospitable terraces with a life of their own that have become an archipelago of *dolce vita* since it has left the Via Veneto and has started withdrawing from the piazzas.

"Come after dinner, any time after ten. Press the number 10 button on the *citofono*. Let's chat a little" is the standard invitation. The number of the apartment is important because fear of burglars, robbers, kidnappers, and terrorists has prompted more and more householders to take their nameplates off front entrances. There will be drinks, and anyone who brings a special bottle will be particularly popular. The main thing is talk for talk's sake, most probably about the foibles, affairs, and follies of absent friends and acquaintances. No heavy conversation. One may meet new, interesting guests, and possibly find company with whom to end the night at a discotheque.

There was no disco subculture in Rome during the sweet 1950s when Fellini was observing the rites of the Via Veneto café society and the incipient alienation of its intellectual fringe. Now, discotheque dancing and rock—together with motorcycles—are infatuating the very young in Rome. Juveniles dominate in many discos, intolerant of the undaunted middle-aged dancers who pathetically try to win their acceptance. Fellini's Romans were mellow, not adolescent, sensualists.

Also new is the alarmingly vast Roman drug scene, which reaches into discos and nightclubs, as the many busts show. One recent raid was aimed at a tearoom-disco for women only, the Zanzibar in the Trastevere section, but it eventually turned out that the police had no case. Roman parks and other places where junkies congregate are full of throwaway syringes. At the time of *La Dolce Vita*, mainlining in Rome was almost unknown, and any use of narcotics was an exoticism, a depravity of foreigners or of rich, cosmopolitan Italians.

Fellini's film barely hinted at the existence of a gay Rome.

Now it is out in the open and thoroughly self-assured. In a gossip-loving city, the extent of social acceptance can be gauged by the yawns a guest at a party will elicit by mentioning that some personage, maybe a government member or a Vatican prelate, really is *frocio,* a homosexual. Oh yeah? Several gay nightclubs are in business, like Easy Going, just off the Piazza Barberini, its decor a self-mocking imitation of the street urinals that are known as *vespasiani* because Emperor Vespasian, always searching for new revenues, put a special tax on them.

If for Fellini the true Via Veneto was the plywood-and-plaster movie set in Studio No. 5, it is getting seedy there too. Cinecittà really is where the sweet life was born as the cynical and sensual escapism of a very small Fascist elite in the 1930s, just as Mussolini was sending his troops to fight in East Africa and Spain. The Fascist regime's "cinema city" was inaugurated in 1937, the year after the conquest of Ethiopia, on 130 acres of land on Rome's southeastern outskirts that had belonged to Prince Torlonia. The rich prince, whose ancestors were bankers to the popes, was also the owner of Mussolini's rent-free private residence on the Via Nomentana.

Il Duce himself was a movie buff. In a room in the Villa Torlonia he and his family regularly had private screenings of films, including American imports that Mussolini, as the supreme censor, judged inappropriate for his nation and did not permit to reach the country's cinemas. The dictator's older son, Vittorio Mussolini, had an ambition to be a film producer. It was the "white telephones" era in Italian motion picture history. The immaculate bedroom phone was a visual symbol for the imaginary sophistication of an urban society pictured in bland movie comedies for a still prevalently rural people. Influenced by his son, Mussolini favored the Cinecittà project, convinced that the capital of his new Fascist empire must also be a center of the modern art form of the cinema.

Mussolini's interest in the motion picture industry grew

even more when the younger sister of Clara Petacci, his mistress, discovered a vocation for acting in films. As a budding star, the sister transformed herself from plain Maria Petacci into the exotic Myriam di San Servolo. There was no problem about financing a film with the dictator's quasi-sister-in-law as the lead. However, Roman cinema audiences guffawed and booed when it was shown, and it was quickly withdrawn.

Several other actresses of more talent who became stars in Cinecittà were the girl friends and protegées of high Fascist officials or, as the parlance then was, of "hierarchs." Until late in World War II, the studio complex turned out propaganda films.

The Allied armies that liberated Rome from the German troops in June 1944 used Cinecittà as a staging area. For some time, suspected Fascist and Nazi war criminals were held in what earlier had been the dressing rooms of film stars. By 1950, a spruced-up and enlarged Cinecittà was back in the movie business, and the roaring years began.

The Americans were coming. The facilities, the skills of the support staffs, the cheap manpower, and the sunshine for outdoor shooting attracted Hollywood producers. One of the little-paid extras in *Quo Vadis* in 1952 was a buxom young girl from Pozzuoli near Naples, Sofia Loren. In 1954, *Time* magazine showed "Italy's Gina Lollobrigida" on its cover with the subtitle "On the Tiber's banks, a new Hollywood."

At the height of Rome's movie boom, Cinecittà didn't seem sufficient, and a producer who thought big, Dino de Laurentiis, built his own cluster of studios on the southern outskirts. Inevitably it came to be known as Dinocittà—Dino City. But rising costs and financial troubles in Italy, the crisis in Hollywood, and the advance of television everywhere forced the Roman film industry to think small again.

De Laurentiis sold his Dinocittà to real estate interests and moved to the United States. Ten years after *La Dolce Vita*, Cinecittà had a brief flurry with another Fellini venture, *City of Women.* Then the cinema city relapsed into lethargy amid public speculation as to whether it would be taken over by the state broadcasting system. Or would the subdividers have the last word? Good-bye, *dolce vita.* Hollywood-on-the-Tiber proved to be only an episode, not an epic.

ON THE BEACH

A couple of longtime residents of Rome drive out to visit Russian émigrés who have found temporary shelter in the seaside suburb of Ostia. Unsuspected trouble is lurking.

The Russians of Ostia are by and large Jews who have been allowed to leave the Soviet Union, often after years of harassment, and who have decided to seek admission to the United States rather than to proceed to Israel. From Vienna, the first stop for virtually all Jewish émigrés, those who have opted for the United States are taken by private relief organizations to Ostia for processing by the American consulate in Rome. Thus Ostia, the beach community closest to the Italian capital, has for years been playing host to a Russian-Jewish colony of, usually, several hundred transients awaiting clearance. The process may take months, and meanwhile the émigrés have to live somehow and to adjust to capitalist society.

Romans have become used to the *Russi* and their outlandish clothes, made for a harsher climate. Some émigrés are always clustering outside the American consulate, which adjoins the United States embassy on the Via Veneto. Others can usually be found at the Porta Portese flea market, where they sell off trinkets and other property that they were allowed to take with them when they left the Soviet Union. Evenings, they are all back in the ramshackle Ostia buildings that have been assigned to them. They sleep four or more to a room.

Relations between the émigrés and local residents, many

of whom commute to jobs in Rome proper, are not cordial. The visiting couple who call on a family from Odessa hear tales of rip-offs by Ostia stores taking advantage of the new-comers. Afterward, the couple themselves do some shopping at a small supermarket nearby. In five minutes they have all they want, check out, and go back to their car, which is parked in the square in front of the store. They find that a door and the luggage compartment have been forced open and the paint is badly scratched. Thieves were looking for loot, and when they found there was none to speak of, they damaged the auto body—all in five minutes.

There are scores of people in the square, but they all look blank, and when two or three are asked whether they noticed the thieves, they say sullenly they didn't see a thing. While the car's owner is questioning the supposed witnesses, his companion shrieks. A youth, maybe seventeen years old, has grabbed her handbag and run off, not even very fast, rather as if he were doing his jogging exercises. Nobody in the square says a word or makes any attempt to stop the robber. The victim feels faint, a kind of shock, walks into the store that is closest to her, a cleaner's, and asks, could she sit down for a minute and maybe have a drink of water? The elderly woman in the cleaner's shop wants to know what has happened, and the visitor tells her. The woman in charge of the store says, "Oh, yeah?" and calls a little boy from the court-yard and whispers something to him. The boy exits and is back in a few minutes, with the handbag. The money, of course, is missing, but the visitor's keys, driver's license, and other documents are there. "That's all I can do for you," the woman of the cleaner's store says gruffly without further explanation. "Thank you," the couple reply and drive off in the damaged car.

To recover from the nasty experience, they stop in Ostia Antica. The ancient seaport is now two miles inland because the Tiber River has silted up that much water space in the fifteen centuries since the decline of the empire and its naval installations. There is a charmed peace amid the ruins of the

Roman maritime city that must have bustled with a cosmopolitan population of tens of thousands when it was flourishing.

A woman archaeologist explains that the remains of several *insulae,* or city blocks, indicate that 1,800 years ago some buildings on streets in a grid pattern were five and six stories tall, the high-rises of antiquity. Now there are hardly any visitors in the vast excavation area, and no purse snatchers.

A police officer later comments: "You live in Rome, you ought to know. Modern Ostia is an unsafe place, especially north of the railroad station. We can't have a patrol every thirty meters. Ostia is full of junkies, pimps, bullies, thieves, and small-time gangsters; they terrorize the other people who live there. Lately some mafiosi from Sicily and Calabria have moved into Ostia. A few years ago, on a tip, we raided a seaside apartment just in time to prevent an Arab terrorist commando from shooting down an El Al airliner as it was taking off from Fiumicino Airport nearby. The terrorists had installed a launcher for sophisticated rockets on the terrace of the apartment."

Maybe fifty thousand Romans live in modern Ostia all year round. They grumble about the service of the local railroad and the subway extension that are their lifelines to the city center, and they try to cope with poverty, narcotics addiction, and crime in their midst. From May to October many additional thousands of Romans migrate to Ostia-Lido, as the seaside suburb is officially called; on summer weekends the invaders by far outnumber the permanent residents. Ostia beach isn't for the queasy. The water is fouled by the largely untreated wastes of Rome that pour out of the Tiber's mouth, and by the tankers that unload their oil there. At the beginning of the warm season the authorities always warn that large stretches of the sea off Ostia are a health hazard, but little is done about it.

Bathing in Ostia was popularized by Mussolini. As often as the weather and his schedule permitted, he drove to the beach for long swims. The "Highway of the Sea," which runs from the western outskirts of Rome to Ostia-Lido—one of the world's first motorways when it was built—permitted the dictator to leave his office in the Palazzo Venezia and reach his favorite spot on the coast in twenty minutes. With today's traffic the trip takes at least double that time. Il Duce used to swim out from a bathing concession that is still in business, La Vecchia Pineta (The Old Pine Grove). The pine trees after which it is named still border the coastline, but they look sickly, and many of their needles are brown instead of green, probably a consequence of constantly being sprayed with polluted sea water by the breeze. Whenever Mussolini turned up at La Vecchia Pineta, an elaborate charade was played. Ostensibly, the ruler of Italy was just another paying guest, but many of the bathers in casual poses around him were bodyguards of the *presidenziale,* or presidential police, a special security force for the protection of the dictator.

It seems that it was on the beach of Ostia that Mussolini first met Clara Petacci, the young daughter of a Vatican physician, who was to become his mistress and who died at his side after Communist partisans captured the couple in northern Italy in April 1945. If the young woman was really introduced, or introduced herself, to Il Duce at the bathing concession, as some of his biographers maintain, she had surely been vetted by the secret police, and the meeting must have been arranged.

Years later, Pietro, a burly lifeguard who used to be in charge of Mussolini's dressing room and watch him when he was swimming, was still in service at La Vecchia Pineta. He probably remembered a lot about the dictator and his girl friends, but he wouldn't talk. He must have been one of the few people who had known Mussolini who did not write a memoir. Pietro also exercised his much-appreciated discretion with the many other love affairs and erotic intrigues he witnessed in the late 1940s and early 1950s when La Vecchia Pineta was a fashionable playground for well-to-do Romans.

Aficionados would rent cabins for the entire bathing season in the preceding fall. Patrons used to linger in their dressing rooms, lie lazily in the sun, enjoy long picnic lunches, and take siesta snoozes in the shade. Very few people would go in the water before eleven A.M., and everybody was out by one. Virtually nobody bathed again before four.

For Romans, it is a health dogma that one mustn't go near the water for at least two hours after a meal or even a light snack. Beaches close to the city are forever ringing with anguished cries from mothers: "Mario, get out of the water immediately, do you hear me? You ate your banana only an hour ago!" Romans watch in horror and amazement as visiting foreigners have ample seaside snacks, then plunge into the waves, swim lustily, and come out alive. Throughout the warm season, the local newspapers regularly carry headlines with variations on "Swims Right after Lunch and Is Killed by Heart Attack."

When La Vecchia Pineta was at the pinnacle of its fortunes, it was inconceivable for most Romans to go to a "free" beach outside a bathing concession. To this day it is not easy to get a glimpse of the sea from the Ostia waterfront, obstructed as it is by an endless parade of bathing cabins in blocks of concrete, plaster, or wood, shower stalls, restaurants, cafeterias, and other money-making amenities. In the late 1970s a liberal Roman magistrate challenged the right of bathing concessions to sell tickets for access to the sea. This brought about court decisions ruling that, since the seashore was public land, anyone may bodily occupy the section of the beach that lies within five meters (sixteen feet) of the waterline. Since then the concessions may reserve their cabins and other facilities for paying patrons, but may not bar people from the part of the beach closest to the sea.

The sand on the "Lido of Rome" is not golden like that on the original Lido, the island barrier between Venice's lagoon and the Adriatic Sea; it is a dark gray. The dull color is due to a high iron content, a circumstance that prompted Mussolini, the beach habitué, to order extraction of the metal for industrial and armament purposes, since there isn't much iron ore anywhere in Italy's subsoil. At the height of the dictator's campaign for economic self-sufficiency before and during World War II, the Fascist newspapers in all seriousness printed photos purporting to show mining of the iron in the sands of Ostia. Some metal was indeed produced in the process, but it wasn't sufficient to put together a single light tank. Today, Italy boasts steel mills whose size would have satisfied Mussolini's desire for industrial power, but the iron in the dark sand of Ostia remains there.

What's new, besides free access to the seashore even near bathing concessions, is naturism. While there are few recognized nudist camps in Italy, and none in the vicinity of the capital, skinny-dipping is now tolerated in certain areas. There are degrees in the accepted exposure of epidermis. On the beach of Fregene, north of the Tiber mouth, now much more fashionable than overcrowded Ostia though almost equally polluted, it is all right for women to take off their bikini tops. Total nudity for either sex is the rule in some spots south of Ostia, such as Capocotta and Torvaianica.

To older Romans, the two names bring back memories of one of the biggest and most piquant scandals the city has known in their lifetime. To this day it is not clear what actually happened. The bewildering sequence of events and wild speculation started in April 1953, when the body of a young woman was found at a lonely spot on Torvaianica, the beach south of Rome. She was identified as Wilma Montesi, twenty-one years old, the daughter of Roman lower-middle-class parents. She had disappeared from their home a few days earlier. The coroner's verdict was death by drowning. There was never any satisfying explanation why Wilma, who had been engaged to marry, had gone to the seashore in cool spring weather without telling her family. Pictures taken of her in her lifetime show a dark-haired, good-looking but not really beautiful young woman wearing the resentful expression that Roman girls of Wilma's social class often assume when they are subjected to unwelcome attentions by men. Maybe she didn't like photographers.

It is not clear how the first rumors started, linking Wilma Montesi's mysterious death with Gian Piero Piccioni, a son of Christian Democratic leader Attilio Piccioni, then the foreign minister. Soon Romans told one another in ripe detail what really had happened: Wilma Montesi had been the secret mistress of young Piccioni, who was holding a job with the state broadcasting network; the two had been at a drug party somewhere near the coast, maybe in a cottage at a place called Capocotta; the young woman had passed out under the influence of narcotics; her boyfriend and maybe others had panicked, believing her dead, and had dumped her on the beach; the rising tide had done the rest.

The newspapers picked up the hearsay, and the Montesi affair was on. It was to keep the country in turmoil for years, rocking the government and deepening the distrust with which non-Roman Italians regard the capital. For the Italian press, the enigmatic story of Wilma Montesi proved to be an invaluable circulation builder. For once, the newspapers departed from their tedious political pontificating and, having a first-rate homegrown mystery on their hands, pulled out all stops to outdo one another in sensationalism. The unspoken watchword seemed to be: get Piccioni. The son of the Christian Democratic politician insisted he had never even met Wilma Montesi, but he was tried and found guilty by the newspapers long before a court of law ruled that indeed there was not a shred of evidence against him, and cleared him of any responsibility in the death of young Wilma. By then his father had long been forced to resign from government.

The Communist Party and other political groups welcomed the affair as an opportunity for an all-out attack on the Christian Democrats. Young Piccioni was represented as typical of the corrupt system that his father's party had established. Infighting between rival Christian Democratic factions seems to have been a source of the rumors, unproved suspicions, and innuendo that the newspapers, day after day, dished out to their spellbound readers.

For Italians in the provinces, the Montesi mystery was proof of Roman rottenness. The phrase *la dolce vita* was not yet generally current, but the flavor of decadence that it conveys was anticipated by the affair of the young woman of Rome who was supposed to have died under outrageous circumstances, and of people in high places trying frantically to hush up the scandal. The Montesi affair made delicious newspaper copy abroad as well. The London popular dailies seized gleefully, even gratefully, on the "drug orgy scandal," dispatching star reporters to Rome to delve into the murky tale of the "raven-haired beauty" and her double life. On Fleet Street, the scandal was a front-page paradigm of Latin depravity. The special correspondents didn't have to dig very hard to please their editors and readers; they only had to translate the more eccentric allegations and theories that the Italian newspapers were printing.

How Wilma really died was never discovered, despite a chain of judicial inquiries and what the press called "super-inquiries." But the investigators dragged into the limelight a bizarre cast of Roman characters—fake aristocrats, playboys, party girls, scheming and conniving officials, mythomaniacs, and adventurers. Looking back today, the general impression is not so much of decadence as of tawdriness, flimsy institutions, and astonishing disorder.

By the time the judiciary at last wound up the trial, in 1957, the Montesi scandal had all but petered out. Nobody seemed much interested anymore in the main defendant, Gian Piero Piccioni. His acquittal was a foregone conclusion, and was formally requested by the public prosecutor, who admitted he had no case. What had been proved, most Italians felt, was that strange things were happening in Rome, a place where money, sex, politics, and backstage maneuvers combine in a disconcerting mixture.

THE MOTHERS

A gray-haired woman calls me by name in the Via Frattina, but I fail to recognize her at first, and Roberta says with a pained smile: "You don't know who I am, do you? I've stopped coloring my hair; I don't have the time now." The girlish, lilting voice that struck me at our first meeting, many years ago, helps me identify her. At that time her hair was jet black and she had just become the wife of a physician who was a friend of people I knew. Roberta's voice, at least, hasn't changed. How is she? I ask. And how is her daughter, Liliana? Roberta says, "Every night before I fall asleep I think the best thing for me would be if I didn't wake up again."

Roberta is in a hurry—she says she always is now—and has gotten through only half of a long shopping list she made for her sortie into the city center. However, she does sit down with me at Ciampini's, and over a cup of tea she tells me about her frustrating life and her worries.

Roberta has been a widow for several years. She is currently taking care of her daughter and two teenage grandsons as a result of the breakup of Liliana's marriage. The two boys seem to have problems in school, and almost daily bring rowdy friends home; the boys' mother, high-strung and often depressed, drifts from job to job; the task of keeping the household going with never enough money has fallen entirely on their grandmother.

Roberta says she wakes up at four A.M. almost every morning, starts thinking about her daughter's situation and the

196

trouble with the boys, and is up by six to face another exhausting day. She is one of a growing number of Roman women who late in life shoulder new, heavy responsibilities because their children, after a divorce or some other vicissitude, fob off their offspring on Mamma. It is a novel twist in the local pattern of momism. If, despite many new tensions, the social fabric in the city is stronger than in many other parts of the West, an explanation is the timeless figure of the Roman matron. Roberta, for one, doesn't want to be one. She says it is unfair to cast her in that role but feels she really can't do anything about it.

Roberta herself coped with her share of marital trouble without turning to her mother for help. Roberta's husband was the first to admit he wasn't a very dedicated doctor or a devoted husband. He came from a Roman medical family; his father was a well-known physician who left him and two sisters a small fortune each. Roberta's father, too, was a physician; throughout his professional career he served with the army. Her fiancé graduated from medical school in the last year of World War II, when exams were little more than a formality and every student passed, and instead of starting an internship he was assigned to medical duty with the navy, where he had little to do and little to learn.

After the war Roberta and the young doctor got married, and he established himself as a general practitioner in an apartment given to him by his father. It was near the Piazza Ungheria in the posh Parioli district. Roberta's husband never had many patients and virtually ceased practicing after his father died; he was well off and had no need to. He became convinced he was cut out for politics, and once ran unsuccessfully for the Chamber of Deputies on the Liberal Party ticket.

His main interest during the last years of his life was a mistress of whom he seems to have been very jealous. He told Roberta, who knew about the affair from the beginning, that he wouldn't leave her because of their daughter, Liliana, to whom he was greatly attached. Maybe he promised his mistress he would live with her once his daughter had grown up. It's the typical story married men in Rome tell their girl friends to gain time, whether they believe it themselves or not. Romans like Roberta's husband seem to abhor any clear-cut decision and to need the ambiguity, lies, self-deception, scenes, and guilt feelings that are built into such triangles.

Roberta's husband fell ill with a form of hepatitis that, as he said sardonically when there was no longer any doubt about it, he had misdiagnosed. His end came in a matter of weeks. There was a pathetic deathbed scene at the private clinic to which he had eventually—too late—been admitted. Roberta called his mistress, saying, "You'd better come quickly, I think he wants to see you." He died serenely, his wife and his mistress at his bedside.

At the funeral service someone pointed out the other woman to me. She kept in the background. There was also the dead man's daughter, Liliana, who had just arrived from London, where she was attending a language course; she had missed the melodrama in the clinic.

Liliana had been a beautiful child but developed into a rather plain young woman who often appeared frozen with shyness and had few friends. Roberta was overjoyed when her daughter announced, out of the blue, that she was going to marry the son of a successful pediatrician. Liliana's fiancé, too, had a medical degree and planned to specialize in pediatrics. The wedding was a glittering affair. The religious ceremony took place in the Church of St. Robert Bellarmine, which is fancied by the Parioli set—the "Pariolini"—and a reception was held afterward at the Grand Hotel. It might have been a convention of the Roman medical profession.

During the following years I learned that Liliana had two sons in quick succession and that her husband had become his father's associate in a flourishing pediatric practice. Now Roberta tells me that her daughter's marriage has ended in divorce and bitterness, that custody of the two boys has been awarded to Liliana, and that, to everybody's surprise, their father and grandfather don't care for them and hardly see them.

Roberta says that in spite of all the money her former son-in-law must be making, he is usually late with his child-support payments—if he comes up with the money at all—but that her daughter is too proud to sue him. He never remembers the boys' birthdays, and is said to have turned into the personification of the classic Roman playboy, with a Porsche, a large boat at the marina in Porto Santo Stefano, and a string of girl friends. The gossip magazines have started taking notice of the "brilliant young socialite doctor" who actually is no longer so young. There are rumors that he has another child by some woman, but he hasn't remarried.

Liliana has suffered from the split-up, her mother says. She has tried working as an interpreter in various travel agencies and other businesses, but she doesn't seem able to keep a job for long. She must have had some unsatisfactory, maybe even squalid, experiences in attempts at finding a new companion. Now in her thirties, Liliana has little authority with her boys and is, as her mother puts it, "quite neurotic." Roberta is in effect the chief of a household where cash is always short. By the time her husband died he had spent most of his inheritance; the widow's pension that she gets from the professional organization of physicians lasts only the first week of each month, the maintenance payments from the boys' father cannot be relied upon, and whenever Liliana is between jobs she doesn't earn anything for long stretches. As her sons are growing up and want motorcycles and tennis outfits to keep up with their friends, something will have to be done to force their father to discharge his obligations more punctually. But court proceedings are notoriously slow, and Liliana has not yet agreed to start any judicial action.

Another young father I know, Giulio, is also separated. He complains that he is being "tormented" by his former wife because he can't see his daughter as often as he would like, and there is real danger that he may be barred from seeing her at all. Giulio, who is a claims adjuster in the automotive branch of a big insurance company, has moved back in with his mother since his marriage foundered, and the two talk mainly about what they will do next time they have the girl, now eight years old, to themselves.

Giulio's former wife officially has custody of her daughter, but she has actually passed the girl on to her own mother, who lives in a small apartment near hers in the World Fair district. The marriage didn't end in divorce but through a church annulment that was routinely sanctioned by a state court. Giulio's ex-wife has excellent connections in the Christian Democratic Party, in the Vatican, and in the legal profession, and it was easy for her to obtain the assistance, almost free of charge, of a leading expert on canon law when she wanted to get rid of Giulio.

I was one of the two best men at Giulio's wedding in the romantic church on the Palatine Hill. A *monsignore* from the Vatican officiated. I didn't know the couple well, but Giulio had asked me to help him out, and it is bad form in Rome to say no on such an occasion. I gave the newlyweds a watercolor that Laura, my decorator friend, had found for me and that I would have liked for myself. I should have kept it; Giulio's wife now has it. At the reception after the church rite I met Giulio's in-laws, who were unmistakably snubbing him. Later I heard that they and their friends were accusing Giulio of having planned his marriage as a Machiavellian scheme to get ahead in his company.

The fact is that Giulio's former wife has for many years been the personal secretary of an executive who is now the director-general of the company where she works. She is regarded as a power behind the scenes of the organization. She knows the best lawyers, top bank managers, politicians, and cardinals. Soon after their daughter was born, she must have decided that it had been a big mistake to pick Giulio as a husband.

Giulio complains now that his ex-wife is vindictive and

wants to humiliate him. She hasn't asked for child-maintenance money, and has recently petitioned the Rome civil court to rule that Giulio isn't the girl's father. She has named a lawyer with whom she is often seen as the real father, and may eventually get married to him. Giulio insists that the legal action, rather unusual for a woman with such strong church ties, was brought only out of spite, and that the daughter is his all right. The court has already ordered blood tests and will seek other evidence. If the verdict is that Giulio is a usurper—and a cuckold into the bargain—he will lose his visiting rights. Does anybody care how an eight-year-old child will react to all this?

Cesare, whom everybody still calls Cesarino, although the diminutive sounds ludicrous for a big hulk of a man in his early twenties, has always known who his father is. They have the same broad face and the same gait, feet outward. Cesarino's father is a no-good character who often passes himself off as a successful businessman, although he has never done much else besides mediating deals at the wholesale food market on the Via Ostiense, selling used cars, and defaulting on promissory notes. He has had scrapes with the law on fraud charges and has served time in prison. When Cesarino was born, his mother didn't know that his father had long been married to another woman. He still is.

In the apartment house not far from the Palace of Justice where I once lived, people would cruelly ask Virginia, Cesarino's mother, to tell them once again how she was "a virgin, I swear to the Madonna, a virgin," when she was seduced by the smooth-talking businessman who turned out to be a phony through and through. Virginia's story has several racy chapters. One is how she found out that Cesarino's father was already married and what happened when, with the baby in her arms, she confronted the other woman, who didn't seem to be particularly surprised.

Later, Cesarino's father showed up a few times in our building and for a few months even lived in Virginia's place. The idyll ended abruptly when Virginia found out that the father of her little boy had pocketed money she had incautiously given him to pay the rent. She threw him out.

All these years Virginia has worked as a seamstress and managed to bring up Cesarino virtually without any help from his father. Cesarino wasn't a good student, and people in the building used to say, "What do you expect in such a family situation? The boy will end up like the crook who took advantage of poor Virginia." Yet after his military service Cesarino surprised everyone by his almost fanatical will to work. He never has been idle, although he hasn't been very fortunate either. Recently he landed what he thought was an excellent position as a driver and bodyguard for one of the three Caltagirone brothers, the contractors. But just as he was about to start service and had already given up a poorly paying job in a storehouse on the city outskirts, his prospective employer left Rome in his executive jet and was later arrested in the United States.

The disappointment over the vanished *sistemazione* with the Caltagirone empire threw Cesarino into a deep depression, and his mother told neighbors she was afraid he might commit suicide. He didn't, though, and soon started job-hunting again. He even applied for a job with the Carabinieri, who need recruits for their fight against terrorists, but he was turned down on the ground that he was born out of wedlock. The military police corps still has such archaic regulations.

For a few weeks Cesarino toiled as a bricklayer at a construction project, although he lacked experience in such work. Eventually he found a job as a bellman in one of the new hotels that do business mainly with travel groups. He likes the place and has started to learn English in the hope of getting promoted to the front desk.

He also talks about getting married; he has for quite some time been going steady with a salesgirl. Virginia is horrified by the prospect that Cesarino and his future wife will be living with her and may have children whom she'll have to take care of. "I have brought you up all by myself, and I'm tired now," Virginia keeps telling Cesarino. "I don't want to go through all that again now that I am old." Nevertheless, it seems that this is just what is going to happen. Virginia won't lose a son but gain a daughter-in-law—and probably also some grandchildren to keep her busy for the rest of her life.

At first, life with a Roman mother-in-law seemed bliss to Patricia, who is from Ohio. A graduate of Wellesley, she had done research for postgraduate work in Florence and Rome, and had met Luciano, the manager of an antiques store in the Via dei Coronari. Although the long, narrow street between the Piazza Navona and the Tiber is lined with scores of such businesses, Luciano is doing well.

When Pat and Luciano were dating during their whirlwind romance, she was surprised to learn that although he was maintaining a cozy bachelor apartment on the Via Cassia he really lived with his widowed mother. Luciano was then approaching his fortieth birthday. Shortly after that milestone in his life he and Pat got married.

Luciano found a four-room apartment on the same block in the Salario district where his family—his father was a Fascist big shot—had been living for decades. Pat isn't poor and had some money sent from the United States to help finance the purchase of a home for herself and her husband. Her mother-in-law outdid herself to help the couple: she contributed cash to buy and furnish the apartment, did most of the bargaining with tradespeople, and kept after the plumbers and other craftsmen who modernized the kitchen and bathroom.

Now, the mother-in-law regularly sends her part-time maid to help Pat with the housework, and drops in herself two or three times every day to do some cooking for the couple, press one of Luciano's best shirts, take suits and dresses to the cleaners who have served her for many years, or even wash the dishes. She has insisted that Pat call her Mamma. At least once a week she makes what she must think is a subtle diplomatic inquiry as to whether her daughter-in-law is pregnant. Luciano's mother seems impatient to become a grandmother.

"I thought I wanted a baby right away," Pat said the other day. "Now I'm not so sure, and I prefer waiting. The thing is, you know, I've realized too late that I'm not really married to Luciano. I married his mother. One of my biggest mistakes was to go to live near her."

Luciano no longer has his Via Cassia apartment, but Pat suspects he is using a new place, maybe sharing it with one of his many friends, and that his mother knows of the arrangement and has the phone number. Pat says that although Luciano makes a big show of affection, especially whenever they have guests at home or go out for dinner at some trattoria, he is probably having little affairs. Mamma seems to have covered up for him once or twice, corroborating alibis that turned out to be false.

"The worst thing isn't that he's fooling around," Pat remarked with bitterness, "but that he has to tell his mother. He's so much closer to her than to me. At the ripe age of forty-two, Luciano is a little boy who makes no decision without consulting Mamma, even about what kind of suit he should wear. Mamma runs our life."

Sure, it would be a great help to have her mother-in-law around if she were to have a baby, Patricia concedes. Mamma would be the ideal unpaid baby-sitter. "But do I want her to take over my child, too?" the American in Rome asks.

SUMMER HAPPENING

Fatal shooting in the piazza. It is close to midnight, but at least a hundred people are still lingering in the square in front of the Church of Santa Maria that is the heart of the gaudy Trastevere district. There are scores of patrons at the tables of the two outdoor restaurants; characters who may be junkies are sitting on the church steps and around the fountain at the center of the piazza; a small crowd is milling around.

White-uniformed city policemen lean against motorcycles, and small cars guard the approaches to the piazza. City hall has just started another "Tranquil Rome" program and ordered its cops on overtime to curb noise, rowdiness, and crime and to enforce the long-ignored ordinances that ban motor vehicles from certain areas. The Piazza di Santa Maria in Trastevere is one of the pedestrian malls set aside by the city fathers as islands of quiet and relaxation for residents and tourists.

The square has lately been overrun by drug addicts and pushers, purse snatchers, and weirdos. Trastevere, Trashtevere, say the many foreigners who live in the newly fashionable neighborhood, and Romans with a smattering of English have picked up the nickname. The popular district on the right bank of the Tiber—with its winding streets without sidewalks, its many decrepit houses, and its taverns —has always been a refuge for shady types. The venerable Queen of Heaven Jail on the Tiber embankment nearby is a familiar institution.

One isn't really a Roman, according to indulgent folk wisdom, if one hasn't been locked up at least once in the Queen of Heaven Prison. Quite possibly the percentage of such certified genuine Romans is higher in Trastevere than in any other section of the city.

The neighborhood "Beyond the Tiber" is well up to date on what is going on behind the jail walls. Off-duty turnkeys and the relatives, lawyers, and associates of inmates come and go, and make cryptic phone calls from Trastevere espresso bars. Whenever one of the frequent jailbreaks occurs, the police assume that the escapees haven't gotten very far and may be lying low in some Trastevere hideout. Queen of Heaven is known to be as full of drugs as the Middle East, and the supply base for the traffic is close at hand. Trastevere has been called the Casbah of Rome.

It is also the city's Greenwich Village. Since the end of World War II, young people with unconventional life-styles, artists, and expatriates have moved into the earthy neighborhood. Rents for walk-up apartments with skimpy plumbing and for lofts without any plumbing have soared. An air of spotty sophistication, a few art galleries, off-off theaters, discos, and a flood of tourists have come to Trastevere.

The district has always taken pride in its separateness from the rest of the metropolis. For many years it has celebrated its Noantri festival every summer—*noantri* meaning "we others" in the particular Trastevere vernacular. Lately, the old dialect word has taken on the connotation of an alternative subculture, and the Piazza di Santa Maria is its show window.

On this particular summer evening a battered small Fiat with a young woman at the wheel and a man beside her enters the piazza from its south side, pursued by a policeman who has ordered it to halt in vain. The car traverses the square and runs into another roadblock at its northern exit. The woman driver swerves around the obstacle and steps on the gas pedal. Two policemen fire at the fleeing car, and it stops. When one of the two reaches the car and tries to open its left door, the woman suddenly drives off again. More shots are fired, and the Fiat comes to a halt. The door is opened, and the lifeless body of the woman slumps out; the man who had been at her side has disappeared.

The people in the piazza protest violently against the trigger-happy policemen. Some youths set fire to a parked police motorcycle, and the flames destroy two nearby cars. A hostile crowd gathers. It looks like the start of a major riot when Carabinieri forces, quickly alerted, arrive at the scene and cordon off the piazza and its surroundings. "Move on! Go home, everybody!"

Feverish police investigations during the night disclose that the young woman was driving a stolen car, and that she and her companion were using it to try, unsuccessfully, to rob a young visitor of a handbag. The dead would-be purse snatcher is identified as a drug addict, twenty-one years old, with a record of arrests for petty thievery. Nobody knows who the man was and what happened to him.

The two municipal policemen who fired the shots assert they did so because the woman in the car had tried three times to run them over. Eyewitnesses deny this version of what happened, contending that the Fiat was crossing the piazza full of people rather slowly. The Communist mayor, in a statement, voices shock at "the horrible accident, an absurd death," and extends condolences to the dead woman's family. Inquiries into the shooting are opened. The two city cops are arrested.

One of the questions that Romans ask is why many of the three thousand municipal policemen, who up to recently were unarmed, have lately been equipped with guns. Aren't the thousands of heavily armed Carabinieri and Public Security Guards enough? Is there a need to shoot to enforce traffic regulations? What if the victim was just a careless or inexperienced driver?

For several days there are anti-police demonstrations in the Piazza di Santa Maria in Trastevere and at other sites of late-hour outdoor life, like the Piazza Navona and the Piazza Farnese on the opposite bank of the Tiber.

A traffic cop complains: "Youngsters ride by on motorcycles and taunt me. They yell at me, 'Buffalo Bill!'" A couple of police stations are bombed. The Trastevere shooting and the ensuing tension between the police and young people cast a pall over the latest edition of what city hall regards as its most successful cultural innovation, "Roman Summer."

The program is an eighty-day series of concerts, rock events, recitals, opera, ballet, theatrical performances, movie revivals, chess and checkers tournaments, circus and variety shows, and diverse happenings, some free of charge, others with a nominal admission.

The summer festival is essentially the creation of one man, Renato Nicolini, the young Communist who is Rome's commissioner of culture. The tousle-haired, voluble Nicolini, who serves the city government in blue jeans most of the time, is a graduate of the Christian Brothers' private high school and of the turbulent School of Architecture, which was a major battle zone in the Roman student rebellion of the late 1960s and early 1970s. Few people may care to move into a house built by him, if he ever practices as an architect, but nobody denies his talents as an impresario.

Before Nicolini, Rome's cultural summer life consisted only of rather humdrum outdoor opera performances—mainly *Aïda*—in the ruined Baths of Caracalla, and the equally shopworn open-air concerts in the huge shell of the Basilica of Emperor Maxentius. Both series of offerings were principally aimed at tourists, who nevertheless kept lamenting that there was little to do in Rome on summer evenings after a hard day of sightseeing.

The new Communist city administration brought in Nicolini as an idea man. He argued that not only tourists but also the many Romans who spend the summer in the city were entitled to organized entertainments and new artistic experiences. The commissioner also insisted that cultural activities should be decentralized so that every neighborhood could benefit, and that it was wrong for the city to take care only of traditional opera and classical concerts while neglecting popular culture and experimentation.

On a budget of just $1 million, the city's dynamic culture commissioner has provided opportunities for the city—and especially for its young people, who can no longer complain they are bored—to see film classics, listen to good jazz and seldom-performed classical music, watch modern-dance troupes, and take part in an open-ended poetry festival. The outdoor marathon of poets and would-be poets is one of Nicolini's proudest triumphs, meant to be expanded in coming years to include musicians, science-fiction writers, and other talent. "Everyone is welcome," the commissioner says. "Let anyone who wants to become an artist or writer take part!" The result, so far, has been a minor Roman Woodstock, a chaotic, sometimes funny, sometimes tedious, monster amateur night before a participatory mass audience.

Another Nicolini idea is a staccato of "blitz concerts" by small music groups who turn up to improvise at bus stops, in the subway, and at neighborhood markets. A "Dixieland on the Tiber" program puts various bands on boats sailing up and down Rome's long-neglected and heavily polluted river. "Living Street" brings jugglers, aerialists, magicians, and other circus people to corners of the city where nothing ever seemed to be happening before.

The latest American rock numbers can be heard in a suburban square near the slaughterhouse that isn't usually a notable setting for musical events. Beethoven's rarely remembered excursion into program music, the *Battle Symphony* on Wellington's victory at Vitoria, is played on the Spanish Steps—with real cannon shots. Plays by Plautus, Seneca, Shakespeare, and Goldoni are given in the Roman theater of Ancient Ostia.

On Tiber Island, between the former ghetto and the Trastevere district, clips from full-length movies, publicity films, and other cinematic shorts are simultaneously shown on no fewer than sixteen large screens. A "Pan-Asian Music Festival" is held in the park of the Villa Torlonia, once

Mussolini's residence. Dance groups from black African countries perform in other city areas. Recorded music suddenly wafts out of manholes in various streets and squares in a scattering of "phono-events."

The intention of the culture commissioner and his aides is to get Romans away from their television sets on summer nights and out again into the streets and piazzas that have been taken over by junkies and rowdies, and to put the city's illustrious open spaces—the Forum, the Janiculum, the Aventine, the Tiber embankments, and others—to new community use. Hundreds of artists and performers get welcome jobs in the "Roman Summer" project, and there is evidence that thousands of young people are becoming interested in something other than motorcycles, or discos, or drugs.

Sure enough, the imaginative culture commissioner has his critics, too. They call him Rome's Communist Nero, who fiddles while the city is being destroyed, not by fire but by neglect. The Radical Party has plastered walls near the Tiber with posters that say "Welcome to Junkets in Filth" (the Italian text uses a coarser word), suggesting the mayor have the fouled river cleaned up before authorizing boating in it. The streets are dirty, many services function badly, and the shooting in Trastevere has raised serious questions regarding public security.

The incident in the Piazza di Santa Maria also highlights the fact that Rome hasn't even begun to come to grips with its alarming drug problem. Firing guns at addicts won't do. Every day, twenty thousand disposable syringes are sold by the city's pharmacies, and experts believe that most of them are used by two or more junkies before being thrown away. Discarded syringes litter many parks and other open spaces, and even fall out of trees. Parents are terrified that their children may pick them up.

Rome needs a bold rehabilitation program for narcotics addicts—as it needs better schools, hospitals, a more efficient police, and more jobs, especially for young people. Meanwhile, city hall is providing free circuses.

A COUNTERCHURCH

A pleasant evening outdoors in a downtown neighborhood that cannot have changed much in the last three or four hundred years. We are sitting at long, plastic-covered tables in the Piazza San Salvatore in Lauro, in the loop of the Tiber closest to St. Peter's on the opposite bank. Raphael once lived nearby, at Nos. 122–23 Via dei Coronari.

We are eating spaghetti and sausages that we have bought cheaply from a nearby refreshment stand, and drinking amber-colored wine from the Frascati hills. Dessert is sliced peaches in wine. We talk a little with the other people at our table, strangers until now. Many of them seem to be acquainted with one another and live in the dark old buildings that huddle on and off the Via dei Coronari—the street named after the florists who once fashioned wreaths in their workshops there. The Via dei Coronari has only recently become arty and affluent, with a proliferation of antiques stores.

There isn't much time for conversation, though, because the film program we've come for is about to start. On four consecutive evenings, four pictures starring Vittorio Gassman are being shown. Tonight it's *Big Deal in Madonna Street,* a spoof about small-time gangsters in Rome who bungle their ambitious heist, with a cameo appearance by Totò, the late great Neapolitan comedian cast as a "perfessor" of scientific safecracking. The revival of the Roman film classic would be worth a trip to some tacky suburban cinema; it's a treat to see it in a congenial setting smack in the city center, for free, where spectators can eat and drink wine.

The big screen has been put up on a frame to the right of the rather pompous neoclassical facade of the church that dominates the piazza. To the left is a convent with noble Renaissance lines. A large inscription on the frieze of the church recalls that it was rededicated to the Madonna of Loreto in the sixteenth century; originally it was a shrine to the Savior. The words "in Lauro" in the name of the church and the piazza are a reminder that in early times a laurel grove distinguished the spot.

In front of the screen, three hundred comfortable metal chairs have been lined up, row after row, as in a real movie house, for spectators who don't care for wine and snacks. Kids have preempted most of the seats and are having a great time. All told, there may be five or six hundred people in the square. Some of them, at the tables, concentrate on their food and only glance up at the screen from time to time, but most are manifestly enjoying the picture—especially the young ones; it is new to them and they are delighted. Tomorrow night Gassman will come in person to discuss moviemaking and answer questions before the last films of the series will be shown. The popular actor, who is of Genoese and German extraction but has become thoroughly Romanized, may also talk politics for a little while, although he isn't known to be an activist. The four-picture cycle in the piazza has been organized by the Communist Party, and he has to show his appreciation somehow.

The alfresco evenings in the Piazza San Salvatore in Lauro are in fact the main feature of the annual "Festival of *l'Unità*" of the Party's Rome-Center section, which comprises the Tiber loop. Some of the ancient neighborhood's residents are third-generation Romans, which is rather rare nowadays. Ostensibly the festival's aim is to boost the circulation of, and raise funds for, the Communist Party newspaper, *l'Unità*. Most other local Party units in the city, and throughout the country too, stage such an event once a year. There is also an annual festival for the Party organ on the national level, held in one of the big cities, with exhibitions on various themes, volunteer participation of show business stars, foreign delegations, and speeches by top Communist leaders.

During the four-day affair in the Rome-Center section, scores of Party members swarm through the neighborhood hawking the day's issue of *l'Unità*. It is a newspaper that even rank-and-file Communists don't buy every day unless they are prodded. *L'Unità* is written in the ponderous style of most Italian newspapers, compounded with Marxist jargon. It is gray and boring, required reading for Party functionaries and political professionals, but unappealing to a larger audience despite a recently beefed-up sports section. Communists who have to subscribe to the Party organ because they are shop stewards in some enterprise or hold some other Party job usually read the sports pages first, glance at the other headlines, and put the paper away.

Its popular cousin, *Paese Sera,* is much more successful than *l'Unità. Paese Sera* was once printed in the plant of *l'Unità,* far out in the eastern end of the city, but it now has its own offices and presses on the Via del Tritone in the city center and is ostensibly independent, although it continues to follow the Communist Party line. *Paese Sera* has a lively makeup, excellent local coverage, a remarkable culture section, and publishes a morning edition and at least two afternoon editions. It sells well because many non-Communists buy it too.

Like almost all Italian newspapers, *l'Unità* is losing money, and it is understandable that a fund-raising drive every year is a necessity. However, the festivals of *l'Unità,* both on the local and national levels, are much more than promotion for a newspaper. They are a periodic mobilization of the rank and file that gives the membership specific tasks to perform, helps develop organizational talents, and fosters—or at least is meant to foster—goodwill for the Communist Party that may pay off at polling time.

In the Piazza San Salvatore in Lauro, a set of large charts of the Rome-Center section shows how the neighborhood voted in the last administrative elections. The Communist Party again came out as Rome's strongest political movement, and the *popolino*—the little people—who are living in the ancient district in the river loop may claim their share of the success. For weeks young Party members have been gathering the data for the charts and done the graphical work.

Other volunteers painted the posters and signs that were disseminated throughout the neighborhood. The secretary of the Rome-Center section and his little staff of unpaid Party workers drew up the program for the festival, secured the necessary permits from the city authorities and the police, got copies of the Gassman films, and called in person on the famous actor-director to talk him into showing up in person.

Someone in the section had to make a deal with a friendly trattoria for running the self-service refreshment stand on four nights. Somebody had to get the audiovisual equipment and an expert to operate it, and to rent the three hundred chairs. There were even printed posters, put up all over downtown in the hope of luring people from outside the Rome-Center section. The free movies were, of course, the come-on. However, before the Gassman films were shown each night, there were panel discussions on a dais in front of the screen. This important part of the festival program had to be carefully prepared. There was work for everybody in the Party section for weeks.

The public debates before the film shows centered on an issue that affects many families in the neighborhood—housing. A freeze on evictions, imposed years ago by special legislation, expired—after several postponements—just a week earlier. Court injunctions ordering tenants to vacate their apartments for various reasons can now at last be enforced. Many such decrees were issued long ago but were held up until now. The authorities have promised that the vacate injunctions will be carried out only gradually, and that householders who haven't found other apartments will be assigned provisional shelter.

No Roman family will remain without a roof over its head, city hall has pledged. However, bailiffs with eviction orders have already shown up in one or two places and unceremoniously put the furniture of the ousted tenants in the street. Scores of families in the neighborhood may soon face a similar experience.

The Communist Party apparatus knows, of course, that many eviction orders are long overdue and have at last been granted by the courts because landlords proved they urgently needed the apartments for themselves or their children, or because the tenants haven't paid any rent for years. A measure of mobility in the housing market is indispensable if the languishing building industry is to be revived. Thousands of jobs for construction workers depend on whether it is legally acknowledged that landlords may under certain conditions free their apartments of occupants. But in the panel discussions in the Piazza San Salvatore in Lauro, the Party representatives squarely defended the tenants' right to stay on, eviction order or not. All the speakers on the dais blamed the government for its failure to provide sufficient public housing. The attacks on contractors, landlords, and the national government brought strong applause from the crowd in the piazza.

There were also a few straight speeches before the films. An orator sent from the Rome federation of the Party blamed the Christian Democrats and their allies for inflation and the rapidly rising cost of living, and warned that the workers wouldn't tolerate any tampering with the escalator clause—the device that automatically ties wage rates to the consumer price index, and thereby perpetuates inflationary pressures. The speaker from the federation also found fault with the government, to perfunctory hand clapping, for what he called the "slavish" way it is backing American policies. Big, hand-painted signs reading "Peace above All" and "Against the High Cost of Living" flanked the dais and the movie screen. At the sidelines of the piazza, fifteen red banners and ten flags in the national colors—green, white, and red—fluttered in the *ponentino,* the mild evening breeze.

The open-air debates have been carefully prepared, even rehearsed, at section headquarters following instructions from the federation. The local Communist leadership decided that the propaganda effort during the festival should focus on the housing problem after several card-carrying members came to the section to talk about their apartment worries. The high-cost-of-living theme was a natural; it is always a surefire argument against the government, any government in which the Communist Party is not represented.

The section secretary and his staff agreed that foreign affairs ought to be soft-pedaled during the four-day festival. The local people aren't interested in international politics, the consensus was, so let's concentrate on the pressing domestic issues.

Active Party members did discuss the world situation during a recent closed meeting at section headquarters when the secretary broached the problem of the Italian Communist Party's relations with Moscow and Peking. The secretary could report afterward to the Rome federation that the bulk of the rank and file supported the top leadership in its line of seeking a prudent rapprochement with the Chinese comrades while continuing to back the Soviet Union in all fundamental questions confronting the "international workers' movement."

However, the secretary also had to let the federation know that a dozen or so of the section's oldest members had shown great misgivings about the Party's recent overtures toward Peking. These old-timers were "Kabulists," the secretary explained—Stalinist diehards who approved of the Soviet military action in Afghanistan, as they had of the invasion of Czechoslovakia in 1968 and of the tanks that crushed the Hungarian uprising in 1956. An official of the federation called a few days later asking for more details on the Kabulists, presumably for a report to the central committee.

The Rome federation regularly receives such information

on the mood among Party members and sympathizers from its more than one hundred sections in the city and its suburbs. This grass-roots organization of the Communist Party and its muscle in the labor unions enables it to produce big crowds whenever it deems mass demonstrations necessary and—what's more important now—to bring out the vote on election day.

All the one-hundred-odd Communist sections have their own offices, if only in basements or adapted garages, and their own phones. Most of them are staffed by Party workers or volunteers from morning to late at night, and keep in close touch with activists in their territory. Thus, the Party apparatus—the Rome provincial federation, the regional committee of Latium, the central committee, the directorate, and the secretariat—is abreast of what is going on anywhere in the capital. Often the Communist Party gets its news more quickly and reliably than the central government does through its rivaling police bodies.

There is no other political force in Rome with such a network for close communication with its base—certainly not the nation's number one power, the Christian Democrats. However, the lack of an efficient Christian Democratic grass-roots organization is to a considerable degree offset by the church. Pastors, assistant priests, monks, friars, and nuns have been around for many centuries; they know how to take the pulse of the population at least as well as the Communist apparatus does. True, the church seeks to influence the people primarily for its own aims, but these often coincide with the objectives of the Christian Democrats. The ecclesiastical presence and power make sure that on election day the majority of churchgoers will vote Christian Democratic.

The setup in the Piazza San Salvatore in Lauro, with the platform for the Communist propagandists next to the ancient church, is symbolic. It represents the two power systems that really matter in the city. Granted, these days the Church of the Savior doesn't often see congregations as numerous as the crowd that has come to watch *Big Deal in*

Madonna Street. Clerical competition in downtown Rome is too strong, there are just too many churches within a few blocks, and the total number of regular worshipers keeps falling off. On the outskirts, the situation is different. Most of Rome's five hundred churches are clustered in the historical center, while the inhabitants of the new, sprawling suburbs often have a long way to walk if they want to hear mass. Nevertheless, church services in outlying districts are well attended on Sundays.

The Communist apparatus is the first to acknowledge the church's redoubtable power to mobilize big crowds when it puts all its resources to work. Top Communists were deeply impressed recently when a statuette of Our Lady of Fatima, brought from Portugal to Rome, was acclaimed by enormous throngs. The sculpture, on tour to various countries that had been organized by devotees of the Virgin Mary, happened to arrive in the city during a campaign for one of the frequent elections, and may have influenced its outcome. The Communist Party's directorate was baffled by the outpouring of religious emotionalism and ordered its experts to analyze what had happened and why an irrational event had exerted such a vast appeal, particularly in the southeastern suburbs, a poor part of Rome where communism is strong. Similarly, the Communist Party federation, on orders from the top leadership, has been monitoring the Polish Pope's efforts to revitalize the city's pastoral system by making visits to different parishes, most of them on the outskirts, Sunday after Sunday.

At present, the church and the counterchurch—the Communist Party—have an organizational problem in common: desertion by the young. While the parish priests are reporting to the Pope's cardinal vicar for Rome that, alas, young people prefer the soccer stadium or the discos to Sunday mass, the Communist sections inform the central committee that their units of the Communist youth federation are losing ground to ultraleft "autonomous" groups.

These *autonomi* deride the section secretaries and their

activists as apparatchiks, criticize the official Communist Party as revisionist and semibourgeois, and claim to be the genuine representatives of Marxism and the proletariat. "The appeal of the *autonomi* to young people who ought to fight in our ranks is our biggest worry," a Communist functionary who must remain nameless confided to me. "They also worry a lot about this on the third floor of the Via delle Botteghe Oscure."

The secretary-general, Enrico Berlinguer, has his office on the third floor of the forbidding building on the Via delle Botteghe Oscure that is the Communist Party's national headquarters. Berlinguer himself once headed the Communist youth federation and was then sarcastically described, because of his habitual gloom and his alleged pedantry, as "the oldest young man in all of Italy." A Sardinian whose family once belonged to the island's petty nobility, the Communist leader is at least as un-Roman as the Polish Pope. In Berlinguer's own home, church and counterchurch meet: his wife goes to mass, and at times the secretary-general has been seen waiting for her outside a church in the north of the city. Whenever Berlinguer is questioned by reporters about this, he says he doesn't want "to discuss the philosophic convictions" of members of his family. In the Rome-Center section, the wives of some Party members are regular churchgoers.

Church and counterchurch aren't so far distant from each other in matters of style, either. The Communist functionary, who will remain unnamed, remarked to me: "Whenever I go to the Via delle Botteghe Oscure I feel the way a devout layman or a priest must feel on entering the Vatican. You have a strong sense of belonging, yet you aren't really at home. You have no friend at headquarters, you are being treated with condescension at best, or you have to justify yourself for something you did or didn't do. You realize you are a tiny cog in a big bureaucratic machine in which so many things go on of which you have no idea."

It has long become trite sarcasm to point out that the

Italian Communist Party has established its national center in what is called, in translation, the Street of the Dark Workshops. The name recalls the cramped quarters where craftsmen were busy in centuries past, and has nothing to do with conspiracies. The neighborhood is heavy with topographical symbolism. A stone's throw away there is the church where St. Ignatius of Loyola, the elitist who founded the Jesuit order, is buried. At about the same distance in the opposite direction is the balcony from which Il Duce used to harangue his "oceanic" multitudes in the Piazza Venezia. The unlovely structure that houses the top Communist hierarchy is said to have been built with the treasure in gold and valuables that Mussolini was carrying with him when he fell into the hands of Communist partisans while trying to escape to Switzerland in April 1945.

Over the years, I have been inside Communist headquarters on occasion, but never got farther than a nondescript hall where Party officials receive visitors. Members of the apparatus, like prelates in the Vatican, don't admit outsiders to their offices but meet them in conference rooms. The caller gets a glimpse of sober corridors with many doors, and the bland faces of functionaries that would go well with the black cassocks of the papal secretariat of state. The atmosphere in the building on the Via delle Botteghe Oscure, the powerhouse of the counterchurch, is distinctly curial. But in the Piazza San Salvatore in Lauro, with batteries of wine flasks lined up, the face of Roman communism is folksy.

A CLUB OF KNIGHTS

The state dinner at the headquarters of the Knights of Malta is in the sixteenth-century palace on the Via Condotti. This is Rome's most elegant street, two blocks from the Spanish Square and nearly opposite Gucci's. The Prince and Grand Master, His Most Eminent Highness Fra' Angelo de Mojana di Cologna, is flanked by dignitaries. The grand master and the elderly noblemen around him, who bear such titles as Bailiff Grand-Cross of Obedience or Knight of Honor and Devotion, are all in dark suits. Their splendid red uniforms, heavy with gold braid and epaulets, and their long black capes with the eight-pointed white Maltese cross have remained in mothballs; they are reserved for even more solemn occasions and religious ceremonies.

The grand master, a poker-faced former Milan lawyer, is supposed to be the highest-ranking layman in the Roman Catholic Church. He is entitled to be addressed as "Your Eminence," like a cardinal, and claims the prerogatives of a head of state.

The guest of honor at dinner in the tapestry-hung hall where the knights usually entertain is the superior-general of the Jesuit order, the Very Reverend Pedro Arrupe, head of the strongest and most influential religious community within the church. At last he arrives—a slightly built, ascetic-looking Basque, the twenty-eighth successor to St. Ignatius of Loyola. He has come on foot all the way from the Jesuit Curia near the Vatican, a thirty-minute walk. And he is wearing a gray civilian suit, with a well-worn, ill-fitting jacket, a white shirt with a badly pressed collar, and a dark necktie.

The knights are flabbergasted. What message does the superior-general of the powerful Society of Jesus mean to convey by showing up without the black cassock that every priest in Rome should wear in public, as the Pope keeps insisting? Does Father Arrupe by his modest, not to say threadbare, secular attire intend to hint that he doesn't think much of the knights' aristocratic and archaic pretensions? The table conversation between the grand master and the Jesuit superior-general is noncommittal, and Father Arrupe soon takes his leave to walk back to his order's center beyond the Tiber, having smilingly turned down an offer to be driven there by one of the knights' limousines with diplomatic license plates.

The almost ostentatious plainness of the Jesuit chief's appearance when he paid an official visit to the grand master will be endlessly discussed in embassies, curial offices, and convents throughout the city. Such are the things that matter to the coterie of diplomats, aristocrats, and clerics around the Vatican. The Knights of Malta supply a generous share of such gossip.

The handful of noblemen in their palace on the Via Condotti, which enjoys extraterritorial status, like an embassy or the Vatican, is an anachronism. The worldwide organization of the Knights of Malta is an international oddity. The charitable work the order does is overshadowed by its claim as a sovereign entity, like a recognized state, maintaining diplomatic relations with governments, striking coins, and running its own mail service. The bestowal of highfalutin titles, gaudy decorations, and ornate robes on social climbers is a major source of income. And yet the quaint little club on the Via Condotti seems to respond to a diffuse craving for pageantry, legitimacy, feudal titles, decorations, and costumes.

Proof of this may be seen in the fact that new groups, some blatantly phony, pop up continually, competing with the Rome-based Maltese order for wealthy members to be co-opted, initiated, promoted to imaginary positions, and honored with fanciful distinctions. The knights of the Via Condotti maintain a special office in their palace to monitor what they call "the false orders of Malta." At latest count there were fourteen of them, including American Masonic organizations. Some of the rivals that annoy the Maltese order of Rome are doubtless part of the transnational underground industry that keeps turning out fake titles of nobility, college diplomas, and documents conferring sham honors.

There seem to be plenty of people who are always willing, even eager, to pay handsomely for such questionable recognition. Rome is one of the world centers of this racket. From time to time the police arrest some adventurer who makes a living by selling parchments that nominate the rich recipient as a marquess, count, or doctor of humanities. In most cases the dealers in phoniness get off lightly because it is hard to prove fraud, and the mere catering to vanity isn't a crime. An upstart manufacturer who buys a diploma of a nonexistent academy or a scroll that in illuminated script proclaims him a baron ought to know he is party to a hoax.

The knights of the Via Condotti are in a class by themselves because so far they have been able to defend their fiction of sovereignty despite the whiff of ridicule that hangs over it, and to keep playing their charades of independent government and international diplomacy. Their official name sounds impressive enough: The Sovereign Military Hospitaller Order of St. John of Jerusalem, of Rhodes, and of Malta. The reminiscences—of early pilgrimages to the Holy Land, the Crusades, the centuries when the knights held territorial power on entire islands in the Mediterranean and battled the infidels—are carefully nurtured. The official list of the seventy-seven grand masters starts with one "Blessed Brother Gerard, the Founder," circa A.D. 1120. One would like to imagine that the Knights of Malta who took part as a distinct force in the battle of Lepanto, A.D. 1571, were of sterner stuff than are the languid aristocrats of the Via Condotti today.

The present grand master is at the top of a government

structure that looks impressive on paper. There are such officers as a grand commander, grand chancellor, hospitaller, receiver of the common treasury, and advocate of state; other worthies serve on bodies that are called court of accounts, tribunal of first instance, and tribunal of appeal. What's lacking is territory. Although the palace on the Via Condotti takes up half a city block, it just isn't big enough to make a credible ministate. It isn't even extraterritorial in its entirety: the fashionable haberdasher and other stores on the ground floor that pay high rents to the knights aren't exempt from Italian laws. Liechtenstein and Monaco at least can control their own shopkeepers.

The core of the Order of Malta is a group of thirty-five aristocrats, most of them well over fifty years of age, who have taken vows of obedience, chastity, and poverty, like friars. They are under no obligation to live in common. In fact, some of them live in well-appointed homes around the city or elsewhere and put up in expensive hotels when they travel.

The Vatican nevertheless regards the thirty-five "professed" knights as a religious community. On one level, the knights who have taken vows are subject to supervision by the Roman Curia's Sacred Congregation of the Religious, which is the papal administration's department in charge of monks and nuns; on another level, they deal with the Holy See through a legation, like an independent power. This dual status breeds ambiguity and leaves plenty of room for maneuver. There is no other situation like this in the whole Roman Catholic Church.

During the 1950s, a faction in the Curia was pressing for tighter Vatican control of the Maltese order. The campaign started after the death of the seventy-sixth grand master, Fra' Ludovico Chigi della Rovere Albani, who, with his white beard and black eye patch, was immensely decorative.

A formidable Vatican prelate, Nicola Cardinal Canali, spearheaded the crusade for the takeover of the order that Prince Chigi della Rovere Albani had headed. Cardinal

Canali, who used to wear a black wig, was himself the grand master of a rival group that claimed to perpetuate the traditions of Christian chivalry, the Knights of the Holy Sepulchre, distinguished by their white capes. There was a web of cabals and intrigues on all sides. For ten years, the beleaguered knights of the Via Condotti were prevented from electing a new grand master. Pope Pius XII set up a special tribunal of five cardinals to redefine the order's status, and the interregnum ended with the election of the seventy-seventh grand master, Prince de Mojana di Cologna, in 1961.

The main reason that prompted Cardinal Canali and his faction to mount their unsuccessful offensive against the Knights of Malta was apparently their wealth. In Rome, the order owns not only its Via Condotti headquarters, conservatively valued at $100 million, but also a complex on the Aventine Hill composed of the large Palace of Rhodes, a church, building annexes, and gardens. The compound on the Aventine, a Roman landmark with a celebrated panorama, is the seat of a Maltese "grand priory," or local subdivision, but is used by the order's top leadership for ceremonial functions.

How rich the order really is cannot be determined from reading its publications or interviewing its officials. "Everybody always asks us that question," a dignitary in the Via Condotti complained when I asked about their assets and budget. He didn't come up with a straight answer. The order's grand priories of Lombardy-Venice, Naples-Sicily, and Austria are known to own much property too. The order's biggest source of income may be its select membership of about ten thousand, many of them very wealthy.

The headquarters in the Via Condotti divides its chivalrous ranks into three classes. The top group is made up of the thirty-five professed knights, those who have taken the vows of obedience, chastity, and poverty. The second class comprises knights who have promised "to strive for the perfection of Christian life." The bulk of the order is composed of members who take no vows and make no formal promise but are merely expected to conduct Christian lives and devote their energies to the service of the organization. This third class is subdivided into six categories and includes women, who may be "dames of honor and devotion," "dames of grace and devotion," and "dames of magistral grace." All members, men and women, are entitled to wear the black cape with the Maltese cross. New knights and dames pay a $1,200 initiation fee that is called their "right of passage." The order periodically canvases the membership for contributions to help finance its welfare projects and administrative expenses.

The Knights of Malta run a two hundred-bed hospital on the southwestern outskirts of Rome, an outpatients' ward in a wing of the Via Condotti palace, and a string of medical and relief services in various parts of the world. Local units of the order—its grand priories and national associations in several countries—also organize the transportation of sick persons to the shrine of Lourdes, France, make occasional cash donations in emergencies, and play a role in aid to refugees. Yet the impression prevails that a disproportionate part of the knights' considerable resources is being spent on representation and the trappings of sovereignty—diplomatic missions, pageantry, and official trips by dignitaries.

To keep the headquarters in the Via Condotti going costs around $600,000 a year, the order says. What its top officials are paid is undisclosed, but some of them who are independently wealthy may only be drawing expense money. The bureaucratic machinery of the Knights of Malta provides a chance for retired diplomats of various nations to go on playing pseudo-official roles and enjoying the privileges they are used to.

Thus, when Austria replaced its ambassador in Rome, Prince Johannes von Schwarzenberg, he underwent a metamorphosis into the minister of the Maltese order to the Italian government. He died in a car crash, and a retired French diplomat became his successor. The knights are careful never to appoint an Italian as their representative to Italy. But when the order needed a new grand chancellor—the dignitary who is compared to the prime minister of a state government—it co-opted a retired Italian ambassador to the North Atlantic Treaty Organization and obtained a Vatican dispensation for him because he happened to be married. His predecessor for ten years was a Canadian who earlier in his life had been a vice-president of the Canadian subsidiary of Seagram's, the distillers. He too was married, although in theory the grand chancellors should be chosen from the professed members, who are celibate.

The Knights of Malta maintain formal relations with more than thirty countries, from Argentina to Venezuela. The order's diplomatic corps is rather bizarre; aristocratic names and fancy titles abound. The ambassador to Somalia lives in Rome, the ambassador to Senegal in Switzerland, the ambassador to Portugal in West Germany, and the minister to Cuba in Peru. A predecessor of the order's envoy to the Communist government in Havana did reside in Cuba. When I once was to interview Prime Minister Fidel Castro and was taken by his aides to a sugar plantation near Camagüey in the island's interior to meet him, we drove past a *finca*, or rural estate, that was marked by large signs proclaiming it as EXTRATERRITORIAL—RESIDENCE OF THE MINISTER OF THE SOVEREIGN MILITARY ORDER OF MALTA. A neat way of protecting privately owned land in a socialist system.

One might imagine that the ambassadors, ministers, and counselors of the Knights of Malta aren't overworked, especially when they don't live in the countries they are accredited to. However, they ride in cars with diplomatic plates and travel on diplomatic passports issued by headquarters in Rome.

The knights maintain diplomatic relations with the Republic of Malta, but their dealings with the socialist government of the island, which they ruled from 1530 until Napoleon expelled them in 1798, are brittle. Prime Minister Dom Mintoff appears to think that the order's welfare activities, such as they are, help to make Malta's name known around the world. On the other hand, Mr. Mintoff harbors no love for the order's clerical, conservative, and aristocratic image, and seems to think little of its claims to sovereignty. Malta has more than once suggested that the order move its headquarters back to the island, but the knights have remained deaf to such siren songs and stay put in the Via Condotti palace.

The countries that have formal ties with the Knights of Malta usually entrust their envoys to the Holy See with double representation. Thus, diplomats who have presented their credentials to the Pope show up in the Via Condotti a few weeks later, are received by the knights' master of ceremonies and secretary for foreign affairs, and hand their letters of credence to the grand master. In June each year, around the feast of St. John, the patron saint of the Maltese knights, the grand master offers a diplomatic reception on the Aventine. The ambassadors turn out in their uniforms with sashes and decorations, their ladies in black lace mantillas, to be gravely welcomed by the ranking knights in their red-and-gold gala uniforms.

Such ceremonial affairs, the state dinners, the missions to countries around the world, the occasional ambulance donated to Paraguay or serum sent to the Philippines, cost money; it is understandable that the order is always looking for new income. It doesn't earn much with its mint. Its coins in the antiquated denominations of *scudo, tarí,* and *grano* may interest some collectors but aren't legal tender anywhere.

For many years the order has been attempting to raise funds through its postal service, as do the Vatican and such ministates as San Marino and Andorra. The knights have their own mail stamps, featuring the coats of arms of historical grand masters; the values are in *scudi* and *tarí,* like the coins. There is also a blue mailbox with the inscription "Magisterial Posts" at the headquarters in the Via Condotti. The trouble is that so far Italy hasn't recognized the order's postal service. Fortunately, a few countries that maintain diplomatic ties with the Knights of Malta do honor their mail stamps. If you want to get a legal postmark on stamps issued by the order, all you have to do is write a letter or postcard to a friend in, say, El Salvador, put the knights' stamps on it, and mail it in the Via Condotti. The "Magisterial Posts" puts a bunch of such pieces of mail into a large envelope with Italian stamps and sends it, through the Italian mails, to the general post office in San Salvador, where it is opened, the order's stamps are invalidated with the local postmark, and your message is delivered to the addressee. It's as simple as that. Some philatelists are happy with such a tricky way of getting a postmark of San Salvador on a *scudo* stamp of the Order of Malta, but the procedure is hardly a gold mine for the knights.

In 1979 it seemed that Italy was ready to acknowledge the order's mail stamps. A postal convention between the Rome government and the Knights of Malta was concluded and signed by Italy's head of state and prime minister. Only the signature of the Italian foreign minister, who was ill at the time, was missing. This technicality held up the establishment of regular postal relations between the Italian state and the knights of the Via Condotti indefinitely.

The postal treaty that wasn't put into effect was surrounded by the kind of rumors and maneuvers characteristic of many matters concerning the Knights of Malta. In a petition to the state prosecutor, a group of Roman stamp collectors spoke of possible corruption and demanded a criminal inquiry. "One doesn't have to be a philatelic expert to realize that interests involving billions of lire are affected," they said.

EASTER BLESSING

"*I had tears* in my eyes as I knelt on the cobblestones," said the woman from Milwaukee. "We had been talking about a trip to Rome for so many years, and had always postponed it. Now with the children grown up and my husband in retirement, and with this new Pope in the Vatican, we decided it would be this Easter. We're glad we came."

However, things were a little different from what the couple had expected. The woman was one of the few persons in St. Peter's Square whom I saw dropping to her knees when the pontiff, a small white figure high up on the balcony of the huge church, intoned the Latin formula of the benediction "to the city of Rome and to the world." She got up again rather quickly, apparently feeling conspicuous in her show of a religious fervor not shared by many other people around. Her husband had remained standing, bowing his head while he crossed himself.

The Wisconsin couple appeared baffled when I spoke to them later. "Sure, the Holy Father got tremendous cheers from the crowd, but isn't it all like, what's the word, a happening?" the man, until recently an accountant in a big Milwaukee company, remarked. "Kids close to us kept laughing all the time and let a toy balloon float into the air. Just in front of us, two young people, both in blue jeans— they were French, I believe—were whispering and smooching. A lot of people seemed much more interested in taking snapshots than in praying."

The wife broke in: "And why do the Italian soldiers—they

look handsome enough—have to march into the square, right up to the altar, and exchange military courtesies with the Swiss Guards? What is this, an army parade or the Resurrection of Our Lord?"

The husband said he hadn't understood the Pope's address in Italian, but had liked the way he had said a few words in English and other languages. A young priest from the Netherlands standing nearby winced, instead, at the Pope's display of linguistic skills. "We know he is polyglot," the priest said, "but must he say Happy Easter in Lithuanian and Chinese and Arabic, which he obviously doesn't know? When he tried to speak Dutch, too, he sounded funny." Other Dutchmen in the square had yelled with delight when the pontiff had said Easter greetings in their language. The multilingual good wishes at Christmas and Easter were an innovation by Pope Paul VI, who, besides his native Italian, spoke only French and Spanish really well; they have become a Vatican ritual, aimed particularly at broadcast audiences around the world.

The Milwaukee couple didn't notice it from where they were standing, but just as the Pope was about to speak from the balcony, a young cleric with a white surplice over his plain black cassock held a silver-plated microphone in front of him. The distance from the Pope's face was just right, as was the timing. The pontiff doesn't fuss with the mike or pretend to get entangled in the cord in the playful manner of pop singers.

In addition to many other qualifications, the head of the church is supposed to be a credible and dignified performer in an age of mass media; the cardinals who chose him would not have ignored this aspect of his tasks. For centuries, the Vatican has been in the business of staging impressive spectacles for multitudes of believers, and it has taken to the electronic media naturally and with relish. The deft microphone bearer is today as much a fixture of the papal entourage as the crucifer who since the Middle Ages has been carrying a cross on a tall pole before the pontiff. One suspects that the Switzers in their yellow-red-blue Renaissance uniforms are being retained, despite the Vatican's current economy drive, mainly because they come out well on color television, offsetting the purple of the bishops, the scarlet of the cardinals, and the black of lesser ecclesiastics.

The worldwide media coverage of the Easter rites in Rome provides effective, and free, publicity for the travel business. The number of visitors to the city at this time of the year is steadily increasing. Nobody can tell how many people come for spiritual uplift and for the papal blessing, and how many just because they had a vision of sunshine and pageantry in a historic setting.

Actually, Roman Catholics don't have to be physically present to reap the spiritual benefits of the pontifical benediction; plenary indulgence for their sins on carefully defined theological terms is promised to all those who watch the pontiff on television or listen to him on radio.

Many persons in the throng in St. Peter's Square may not be Catholics, or may not really care much about religion. The majority of those attending the ceremony are clearly from out of town, and a great many are participants in some package trip who behave the way tourists do everywhere, laughing at each other's jokes and reloading their cameras.

The Italian state broadcasting system and the local newspapers will assert later that 300,000 persons were present at the papal benediction, and that Rome had played host to more than a million visitors at Easter. The figures, picked up by news media elsewhere, are wildly exaggerated.

When I started reporting from Rome for the *New York Times,* my bureau chief was an Italian-born American, Arnaldo Cortesi, who held an engineering degree from the University of Birmingham, England, and had a mathematical mind. Annoyed by inflated estimates of the crowds paying tribute to Pope Pius XII that the news agencies put out several times a year, he resorted to simple geometry and arithmetic to prove them wrong. He calculated the entire surface of St. Peter's Square, subtracted the areas—close to the colonnades left and right and behind the two fountains —where one can't see the pontiff, and concluded that no more than seventy-five thousand persons were present when the piazza and the approaches to it seemed tightly packed. We tried to stick to this figure, but to this day, news reports about crowds in St. Peter's Square often speak of a quarter of a million, or even half a million, people.

As for the assertion that a million guests are present in Rome, such an invasion would be an intolerable burden for a city of 3 million. There are 51,000 beds in hotels and boardinghouses of all descriptions in the city and its environs, and maybe 20,000 more beds in pilgrims' hostels, hospices, and convents. Being able to put up and feed about 70,000 visitors at the same time is respectable enough and places the Italian capital in the top rank of international tourist centers.

Roman hotel interests often complain that the church-affiliated guest houses represent unfair competition because they can rely on an underpaid or unpaid work force—their nuns and friars—and avoid, or are exempt from, most of the taxes that hit secular business. The ecclesiastics who offer shelter to travelers retort that theirs is a nonprofit charitable service that has been rendered since early Christianity. Hospices for Frankish, Irish, and Saxon pilgrims, called "schools," were indeed already thriving near the site of the original St. Peter's Basilica before the end of the first millenium of our era.

Today, many of the convents and other church institutions that take in paying visitors are actually running tidy little hotels. The Milwaukee couple had been directed to one of them, not far from the Vatican, by a Catholic travel organization. "Our room is pleasant, the shower works, the water is always hot, the breakfast is good," the Wisconsin woman said. "And when my husband asked for a nightcap yesterday, there was no problem."

All through Holy Week, hundreds of tourist coaches with foreign license plates clog the narrow streets of downtown

Rome, complicating the city's chronic traffic woes. In one behemoth on six oversize wheels, an American woman who lives in Rome and subsists mainly on irregular income from work as a free-lance travel guide sits next to the driver and points out the sights over the public address system for several hours a day. She says: "My working season starts on Palm Sunday and reaches its first peak at Easter. If I am hoarse, it's not a cold but because my voice is giving out." She once was a teacher back in the United States, and says being a tour guide is less tiring, "and it's more fun."

Theoretically, tourist guides must be licensed by the local authorities, but many expatriates without an official work permit get jobs simply because there aren't many Romans who speak foreign languages fluently and are available. The American woman admits that much of what she earns is money that restaurants and souvenir stores pay her for steering her charges to them.

Portraits of the Pope, rosaries, and other religious articles that are to be blessed by him during his audiences, pictures of the Madonna or saints, and devotional literature are big business. Throughout the city, and especially near tourist sights, there is a brisk trade in small replicas of the Colosseum and the she-wolf suckling Romulus and Remus, cheap handbags, kerchiefs with Roman views printed on them, imitation coral necklaces, and machine-cut cameos. Much of the religious and secular kitsch comes from the south; housewives in Naples slum kitchens knit beads, and backyard workshops in Bari turn out plaster statuettes for the Roman souvenir market.

The many junk shops and souvenir stands contribute to the unkempt look that Rome has lately taken on. During Holy Week I have often overheard tourists complain about how dirty the city is, but quite a few of them help make it even dirtier. They picnic on the steps of a church or on a park bench and leave sandwich wrappings and soft-drink cans behind.

Romans themselves are formidable litterbugs. City

officials have lately reprimanded them for their carelessness —to no avail. Rome's current sanitation commissioner, Mirella D'Arcangeli, whose name translates as "Of Archangels," has just lectured her fellow citizens on their filthy habits. "Rome will never be as clean as Vienna, Zurich, or Budapest," she said with resignation, although she promised that better use of manpower and equipment would bring some improvement in a couple of years or so.

The sanitation commissioner has started hiring female street cleaners, who wear blue work uniforms like their two thousand male colleagues, and has disseminated big new garbage containers all over the city. The local press nevertheless keeps denouncing the squalor that envelops noble monuments and once lovely squares, and the neglect that it says is visible everywhere. The sanitation department has ordered its personnel to go to work, even on Easter Sunday, and to wield their brooms above all in spots where most of the tourists gather: St. Peter's Square, the Trevi Fountain, the Spanish Steps, the Colosseum, and the Piazza Navona.

Rome not only doesn't mind cleaning up after its visitors, it is tolerant with them in other ways. The municipal bus system tacitly allows foreigners to ignore the ticket machines into which passengers without monthly passes should put their coins; thus many tourists get free rides. Cars and buses with foreign license plates are often allowed to park in spaces that are banned to local vehicles.

Romans generally are helpful to visitors, volunteer directions, muster every foreign word they know or communicate in body language, show appreciation whenever they are asked questions in broken Italian, and are patient with noisy or drunk tourists. The city has been used to barbarians and invaders throughout its history and long ago learned to take them in its stride.

Today the population is instinctively aware that the tourist business is a bonanza and is becoming increasingly important to its livelihood. Apart from the luxuriant Italian government bureaucracy, the Vatican establishment, the

building trades, and a few light industry plants on the outskirts, Rome has no other substantial sources of income and
must rely on what foreigners spend.

Fortunately for the Romans, the tourists keep coming. But
if only they weren't in such a hurry! Statistics show that
foreign visitors stay an average of 2.96 days in Rome. The
most fleeting guests are the Japanese, whose average so-
journ is a bare 2.03 days. The 400,000 Americans who pass
through Rome every year spend an average of 2.74 days, and
the Germans linger for 3.25 days. Two or three days is
hardly enough to overcome jet lag, much less get to know
the Eternal City. Why can't the visitors learn something
about leisure from their hosts?

TIME IN AN
ETERNAL CITY

A big gun, more than a century old, is still fired on the
Janiculum Hill at noon every day to permit Romans to set
their watches. Its boom is drowned in the roar of traffic, the
keening of police cars and ambulances, and the ordinary din
of a noisy city. It doesn't matter.

Walk down the Via Nazionale and you will notice a clock
on top of a curbside pole marking 11:52, the next one 12:11,
and a third one permanently stuck at 9:23. The Via Nazionale, leading from the ruined Baths of Diocletian to the
western slope of the Quirinal Hill, is one of the city's few
straight, broad thoroughfares. It was laid out toward the
end of the nineteenth century, when the Piedmontese and
other northerners had taken over Rome and tried to make
a modern, efficient capital out of it. Fortunately, they
failed.

RAI, the state broadcasting network, gets astronomical
time piped through an electronic system into its Rome headquarters from an institution in Turin in Piedmont. But
whenever the radio services put the beep-beep signal on the
air, they never tell listeners beforehand which hour and minute it is going to indicate, as if they are afraid the audience
might actually adjust their clocks and watches. After several
short beeps and a long one, the announcer says, "We have
transmitted the time signal marking twelve o'clock and four
minutes." The state network is always having trouble

237

scheduling its programs so that they end just before the full hour, when the time signal is theoretically due.

The bells of five hundred churches, in the baroque piazzas and coach-wide streets of the historical center and amid the high-rise buildings of the modern city sections, peal in mysterious patterns. Some announce morning mass, others mark the canonical hours of worship—tierce, maybe, or vespers—and yet others accompany some liturgical rite. From where I live I can hear the clocks of two nearby churches laboriously striking the full, half, and quarter hours, always off RAI's astronomical time, and always a few minutes apart from each other.

On rare and solemn occasions all the church bells of Rome are heard in unison. It may take ten minutes to get their chorus together, and afterward a few stragglers whimper on when most others are already silent again, but when they all ring in unison, their brass voices triumph over the ordinary street clamor. It happens every time a Pope dies, and the city holds its breath for a moment and becomes aware of history. Romans have a saying they apply to anything that occurs at long intervals: *ogni morte di papa*, "at every death of a Pope." In 1978 the bells tolled twice, at the sudden end of Pope Paul VI's pontificate, and then again after Pope John Paul I, who reigned only thirty-three days, was found dead with a sheaf of papers he had been reading clutched in his cold hand.

The erratic pealing of the Roman church bells is one of the charms of the city. Romans aren't, after all, a split-second people: they regard hours, even days, as approximate units of a creamy commodity that can be spread, squandered, and leisurely enjoyed. Mussolini, who came from the vigorous Romagna region, won foreign praise early during his dictatorship because it seems he made Italian railroad trains run on time. He never succeeded in forcing the habit of punctuality and the skills of time management on the Romans. The languid pace of the capital has not perceptibly quickened in an era of real-time computer services. Indifference to wasted hours, days, and weeks is an aspect of what other Italians keep denouncing as the Romans' *menefreghismo,* a word that may be translated as "I-don't-give-a-damn-about-it-ism."

Listen to the Milan business executive in the Alitalia airliner that flies him back home after a frustrating visit to the national capital: "I took the sleeper train Sunday night to be in Rome early Monday morning," he tells his neighbor on the plane one Friday afternoon. "The train was ninety minutes late. When I called the Public Works Ministry at ten o'clock, the official I had to see either hadn't come in yet or was out for coffee. I got hold of him only on Wednesday, and he fixed an appointment for Thursday. When I went to see him yesterday, I was told he had just been called in by the director-general. I managed to catch him this morning. He coldly informed me that the funds the government owes me have been blocked by the comptroller's office, and that I'd better seek a bank loan to keep going until the money is unfrozen. An entire working week lost."

Similar complaints must have been aired by the procurators of ancient Rome when they came from Gaul or Syria and were kept cooling their heels for months by imperial officials. In a later era, the deliberate slowness of the papal Curia became proverbial. Its imperturbable pace has been adopted by the secular bureaucracy, the legislators, and the law courts of modern Rome.

Roman disdain for rigid schedules and nonchalance about the passage of time may be life-prolonging factors because they avoid stress. The Italian capital demonstrably counts more persons in their eighties and even nineties who are reasonably vigorous than most other big cities.

The Vatican, whose influence on the Roman way of life must never be underrated, even today, has traditionally been a gerontocracy. The longevity of popes, cardinals, and lesser prelates is striking. In this century, Pope Leo XIII died at the age of ninety-three; Pope Pius X lived until seventy-nine; Pope Benedict XV until sixty-seven; Pope Pius XI until eighty-one; Pope Pius XII until eighty-two; Pope John XXIII until eighty-one; and Pope Paul VI until almost eighty-one.

Pope John Paul I, who had never held any curial post, died of heart failure, said to have been brought on by strain—he was apparently intimidated by the formidable Vatican bureaucracy—and self-imposed overwork, at age sixty-six.

Pope Paul VI set off something of a revolution in the Vatican when he decreed in 1970 that cardinals who had reached eighty years of age could no longer take part in a conclave for the election of a new pontiff, and must relinquish whatever posts they were holding in the church's central government. The dean of the Sacred College, Eugene Cardinal Tisserant, a Frenchman who was then eighty-six years old, expressed bitterness, and an Italian prince of the church, Ernesto Cardinal Ottaviani, who was about to celebrate his eightieth birthday and had never given up the gruff bonhomie of his native Trastevere, publicly criticized the pontiff for putting the curial old-timers out to pasture.

The Second Vatican Council, which was held between 1962 and 1965, laid down the rule that bishops all over the world must offer their resignation to the Pope—who may accept or reject it—on reaching the age of seventy-five. There was speculation whether Pope Paul VI himself would step down when he was seventy-five, and again when he was eighty. He did not, and was quoted by a friend, the French Catholic writer Jean Guitton, as remarking that "a father cannot resign."

It is worth noting that the canonical retirement age for bishops, as prescribed by Vatican II, is a decade beyond the sixty-five-year limit for most business executives in Western countries, which tends to be lowered further by some corporations in the United States and elsewhere. Roman civil servants and other wage earners often go into retirement at age sixty, or even earlier, but sometimes do so only to collect their compulsory severance pay and pensions and to start a new job. There is no early retirement in the Vatican, just as there appears to be no voluntary withdrawal from the Roman political establishment.

240

The weighty part played by old men in the Roman corridors of power or, to use local imagery, in "the palace" and in "the room of the push buttons" is similar to the dominance of the aged godfathers and dons in the Mafia.

A politician who wins a government post at, say, age forty is considered a stripling. Only the Fascist regime, forced on an unenthusiastic capital by a non-Roman, Mussolini, stressed youthfulness in public affairs. Its party hymn, "Giovinezza" (Youth), became Italy's second national anthem, together with the Royal March (tará-tará-tará). When Il Duce seized power in 1922 he was, at the age of thirty-nine, Europe's youngest government chief. Twenty-one years later, as his dictatorship was already tottering, he prohibited public mention of his sixtieth birthday. After his downfall in 1943, old men took over again. Marshal Pietro Badoglio was seventy-two years old when he became Italy's first post-Fascist prime minister, and his successor, Ivanoe Bonomi, was sixty-nine.

The deterioration of Roman politics in the 1960s and 1970s, marked by growing disorder and corruption, was in the view of many Italians due in part to the immutable presence of the same gray, aging figures—"the waxworks"—in government and in other positions of power. The heads of state of the Italian republic were in their sixties or, more often, their seventies; President Sandro Pertini was elected as he was approaching his eighty-second birthday. Christian Democratic leaders, like Amintore Fanfani, Giulio Andreotti, and, before being kidnapped and assassinated, Aldo Moro, took turns in top jobs in a game of musical chairs over three decades. The Communist Party leadership, too, had frozen early into a rigid hierarchy of men who had been around a long time, with seldom a new face.

Romans have for many centuries observed the activities and frequent antics of high churchmen who were well on in years, and they possess a keen eye for the foibles of today's aged secular leaders. There is always a plethora of piquant anecdotes about the greed of one prominent personage, the intrigues of another, the dotage of a third, and the senile hatred they all nurture for one another.

Getting old without one's being fully aware of the passing years is helped in Rome by an unchanging rhythm of public events and situations that occur cyclically and are as predictable as the December rains or the midsummer thunderstorms. The Roman year doesn't really start on January 1 but sometime in September, when many people listlessly return from their vacations, and the city, after its August inertia, starts stirring again. Stores that have been closed for weeks are back in business, and their customers, broke because of living beyond their means during the summer, note with horror that all prices have jumped up. The newspapers indignantly denounce what they invariably call the "September sting."

The hunting season opens. Every Sunday thousands of Romans get up before dawn, dress up like Robin Hood, and drive into the countryside to shoot at rabbits and small birds. There is hardly any other game left. Many hunters don't take the trouble to stalk their prey; they fire right out of their cars, and often pepper other nimrods or their dogs with small shot. It may be the last shooting season, because a broadly backed lobby of environmentalists and radicals is pressing for a nationwide ban on hunting.

Schools also reopen, and teachers go on strike for higher pay. Parliament reconvenes after its summer recess, and there is speculation about another government crisis and early elections. Rome is oppressed by a series of sirocco days, but there is hope for the *ottobrate,* the sunny October weeks when the heat subsides and the city is gloriously bathed in mellow light. The Roman version of Indian summer may linger on into November.

The first cold snap touches off quarrels in condominium buildings all over the city on when to turn on the heat. Tank trucks scurry around the city because many building cooperatives and condominiums have not taken the trouble to store fuel earlier, when the price was lower.

Yuletide begins early in December, when the eagerly awaited *tredicesima* falls due. This is the mandatory Christmas bonus in the amount of a month's pay—a "thirteenth" salary —to which every wage earner is entitled. All families with at least one *tredicesima* coming have discussed for months which debts to pay with it and what they will buy if some cash remains.

With billions of lire suddenly injected into the economy just before Christmas, inflation quickens again, and all prices go up another few notches, the "Christmas sting." On December 8, the feast of the Immaculate Conception, the Pope leaves the Vatican to pray at the foot of the column that carries a statue of the Virgin Mary in the Spanish Square. The mayor is there to greet the pontiff. During the following days, suburban types disguised as shepherds from the Abruzzi mountains with robber's hats and sheepskin coats pour into the elegant shopping streets, playing a plaintive Christmas tune on their bagpipes, always the same, and exacting contributions for their seasonal "arrangement."

Christmas trees, most of them imported from Norway and other northern countries, sell briskly, although some priests still deplore the Nordic custom. Many churches display elaborate nativity scenes, some with hand-carved and engagingly naive figures, others featuring religious kitsch with lights that go on and off, plastic angels, Holy Families, shepherds, Wise Men, oxen, and sheep that move for a few minutes whenever someone puts a hundred-lire coin in a slot. Despite television and films, such throwbacks to the Renaissance infatuation with entertainment by tricky machinery still attracts visitors.

The Pope says midnight mass in St. Peter's. Most of the Romans who attend have just finished their family dinner with the traditional Christmas Eve fare—rich pasta, eel or some other fish, and *panettone,* the fluffy Milan cake loaded with raisins and candied fruits that long ago conquered the capital. On Christmas Day the city's streets are deserted; Romans sleep late and indulge in another heavy meal, and tourists wonder what to do.

New Year's Eve brings the usual orgy of fireworks and another epidemic of upset stomachs. Little of consequence takes place until after Epiphany, January 6, when schools reopen after the Christmas holidays, stores start clearance sales, and Romans worry about paying the heaps of bills that have come due. It is the bleakest month, only occasionally relieved by a brilliant *tramontana* day or two.

Easter week means a tidal wave of tourists, and the year's first mass departure of Romans for junketing or traveling. At the beginning of May, the annual international horse show is held in the Piazza di Siena in the Borghese Gardens, regularly marred by heavy downpours. Spring always hesitates to arrive in Rome, and is short. Suddenly, summer is on and the nearby beaches fill up. Quickly, Rome takes on the characteristics of a resort city with people in bright, informal dress parading their early tans.

By the end of July the city empties, although the summer exodus takes place to the accompaniment of strikes and strike threats by railroad and aviation workers, service station attendants, and the personnel of the ferryboats that link the mainland with the Italian islands. Being found in Rome around Ferragosto, the midsummer festival on August 15 that goes back to Emperor Augustus, still means social disgrace to many residents. Most stores, businesses, and restaurants are closed, and the city is abandoned to the tourists. But some of the Romans who love their city best make a point of staying on during the lethargic August weeks. The customary bustle and congestion abate as hundreds of thousands are away on vacation. The magic of Rome that seems to have vanished during most of the year reemerges for the lone stroller who hears the pine trees rustle in the breeze and the fountains murmur in the piazzas.

One notices again monuments that seem invisible at other

times of the year. Romans live amid countless testimonials to 2,500 years of history, but hardly see them. The Colosseum, the triumphal arches and obelisks, the columns and church facades catch the eyes of the local people only when another traffic detour has been decreed because some old stones have crashed to the ground, or when steel-tube scaffoldings go up while the experts are still trying to figure out how the city's historical patrimony can be saved for future generations.

Archaeologists say that air pollution from auto exhausts, vibration from the heavy traffic, and other ecological factors are now causing as much damage to the relics from antiquity in a year as the passage of a century wrought in previous epochs. The industrial civilization of today does at least as much harm to the visible heritage of the city as did the barbarian invasions, the Sack of Rome, and all the other historical calamities it has known. The environmental battle against rapidly quickening decay is a challenge of the next years.

True, the capital of a big, resilient country cannot be expected to become a museum. Yet it may be argued that the historic and artistic treasures of the city belong to all mankind, and that their distracted trustees, today's Romans, bear an international responsibility for preserving what can still be saved. Another few years of dawdling and it may be too late. Even in the Eternal City, time is running out.